Portraits of OUTSTANDING EXPLORERS

By Doris Hunter Metcalf

Good Apple

*This book is dedicated
to my son Sevante*

Portraits of Outstanding Explorers is a resource book of information and reproducible
activity sheets designed to acquaint students with the achievements of people
who, over a millennium, explored North America from coast to coast.
They risked their lives for different reasons: money, fame, power, adventure,
economic necessity, or curiosity. But they all shared an intense,
unyielding desire to discover the unknown.

Executive Editor: Jeri Cipriano
Editors: Lorraine Hoppings Egan and Donna Garzinsky
Portraits: Beatrice Lebreton
Illustrations: Jane Caminos

GOOD APPLE
A Division of Frank Shaffer
23740 Hawthorne Blvd.
Torrance, CA 90505

5 6 7 8 9   MAL   01 00 99 98 97

CONTENTS

Part 1

They Opened the Door

Someone had to be first. Some brave explorer had to go where no one else would dare. It took courage. It took leadership. It took strength to ignore those who said it was impossible. These explorers were the first to open the door to the unknown. They made it possible for others to follow.

BIG QUESTIONS

- Are you a leader or a follower?
- Have you been or would you be the first person to do something?
- How could you gain the courage to meet "impossible" goals?

Ice Age Explorers
(30,000 B.C. to 3,000 B.C.)

Vikings, Italians, Spaniards, and other explorers set foot on America long ago. But they weren't the first—by a long shot. Millions of people were already living in the area from northern North America to southern South America. They were descendants of explorers from another land and another time.

The time was the Ice Age, perhaps 30,000 years ago. A cooler climate turned water into snow, ice, and frozen rivers called *glaciers*. With less water on the planet, sea levels fell. Underwater land forms were exposed. One new landform was a bridge of land between Asia and North America. Today the area is called the Bering Strait.

This natural bridge stayed high and dry for thousands of years. That was plenty of time for mammoths and other tasty animals to cross it. Ice Age explorers followed their "migrating food" into North America. Ice Age settlers followed the explorers. The population grew, and Asians pushed farther south and east into the Americas.

Ice ages come and ice ages go. So from time to time, ice began to melt. When it did, sea levels rose. The Bering Strait flooded once again. The Americans were cut off from their Asian kin. They developed new languages, new customs, and even new physical traits. In the far north, they became Inuits (Eskimos). In the south, they grew into Incans, Aztecs, Mayas, and many other cultures.

Routes of peoples across North America from earliest times

Why aren't Ice Age explorers as famous as Columbus? We don't even know their names! They lived in a time known as prehistory—well before humans could write. Our knowledge is based solely on the things they left behind: pottery, animal bones, campsites, tools, weapons, and so on.

AMERICA, A.D. 10,000

In 8000 years, what might America look like? What artifacts (found items from a culture) will archaeologists uncover? What will the artifacts tell them about today's Americans?

Fast-forward into the far-off future. Then use your imagination. Describe an archaeological site dating "way back" to our twentieth century.

Draw some of the objects found. Tell what the archaeologists thought of these objects and what they concluded about our civilization.

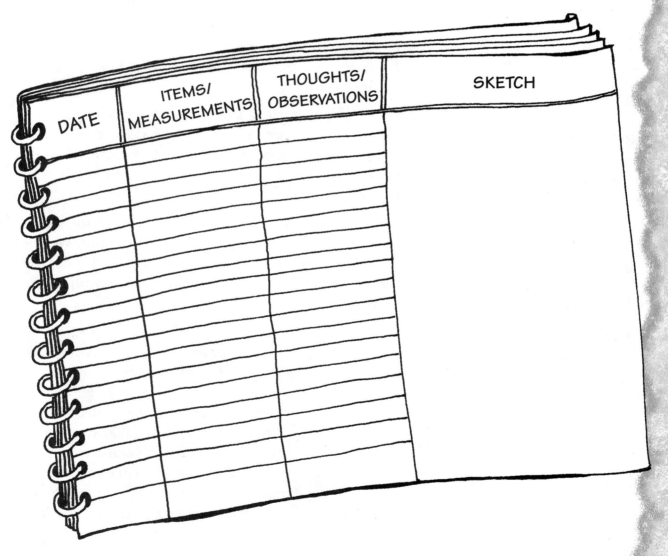

DATE	ITEMS/ MEASUREMENTS	THOUGHTS/ OBSERVATIONS	SKETCH

Leif Erikson
(970s?–1020s?)

MAJOR ACHIEVEMENT:

Erikson set foot in America nearly 500 years before Columbus did. He may have been the first European to do so.

Fact and fiction have a way of changing places over the centuries. Stories told over and over are accepted as fact. Facts get exaggerated as legends grow. That's why, today, Leif Erikson's voyage is part fact and part fiction.

Erikson was born more than a thousand years ago in Iceland. His father, Eric the Red, killed two men and was exiled. During his three-year sentence, he explored Greenland. On this icy chunk of rock, Eric the Red founded a Norse (Norwegian) colony and raised his family.

In about 985, Bjarni Herjólfsson, a Norseman, spotted flat, barren, icy lands west of Greenland. But he didn't bother to investigate.

Fifteen years later, Leif Erikson did. He called this land Helluland or Flatstone Land. Erikson sailed down the coast. The next stop was also flat, but forested. White sand lined the coast. Erikson called it Marland (Wood Land).

Farther south, the crew spotted an island. There they ate wild wheat, grapes, and salmon fish in balmy weather. They named the area Vinland (Wineland) and spent the winter. The explorers returned to Greenland with their ship's hull full of grapes.

Is this story folklore or fact? After Erikson's voyage, Thorfinn Karlsefni, a Norseman, settled Vinland. His son, Snorri, was the first known European born in America. In the 1960s, Norwegians found a 1,000-year-old Norse settlement in Newfoundland. Was it Karlsefni's? Did Erikson's explorations make it possible? No one knows. We do know that the rest of Europe didn't hear about these lands. America remained a secret for the next 500 years.

Vinland (Newfoundland?), 1000?

Greenland

Iceland

ATLANTIC OCEAN

NORTH AMERICA

Newfoundland

Britain

This Land Is My Land

To hold on to their land claims, explorers needed settlers. Eric the Red lured 500 families to a land of ice and rock. He named it Greenland to make it sound more inviting.

Could you lure settlers to the North Pole? Create a travel brochure that highlights all the great things about living there.
There's only one rule: You must
be truthful.

Welcome to

Christopher Columbus
(1451–1506)

In the fifteenth century, educated people knew the earth was round. One fact became clear when a ball was held up: sail west and you'll reach the east—the Far East. The only real question was, *how far* west? Too far, thought most seaman. Christopher Columbus disagreed. The earth was much smaller than people thought, he said. And Asia was bigger. It stretched around the globe, well within reach. Columbus even staked his life on it.

This daring seaman came from the trading port of Genoa, Italy. He knew all about the silk, spices, and other riches in the Indies (India, China, and Japan). He asked Queen Isabella and King Ferdinand of Spain to sponsor a voyage. He asked for three fully-stocked ships, for 90 men, and to be governor of all new land. He asked for the title of admiral, noble (royal) status for his family, and one tenth of the riches. Queen Isabella finally agreed to all his requests. Her cost: $14,000.

In 1492 the *Niña*, the *Pinta*, and the *Santa María* set sail under Columbus's command. When he reached land on October 12, Columbus was sure he had reached the outer Indies. Three more voyages never changed this belief. Columbus died thinking he had sailed to Asia.

The "admiral" had earned his money, his title, and his status. His daring journey had paved the way for other explorers. (One would lend his name to the New World—Amerigo (America) Vespucci.)

Columbus founded a colony to cement Spain's claim in the New World. But the Spaniards mistreated the native people. They enslaved many and shipped some back to Europe. They stole their gold. Thousands of natives died of European diseases. Columbus's legacy, for better and for worse, changed the course of history for centuries.

The "New World," 1492

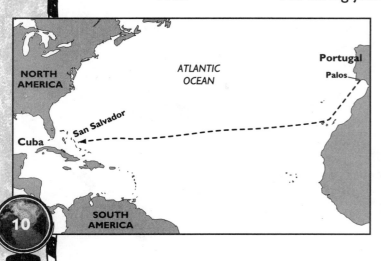

Follow the Leader?

Not all of Columbus's sailors supported him. In fact, many sailors tried to *mutiny,* or take control. How could Columbus convince them not to? If you were Columbus, what would you do or say to them? Choose one of the events described below to write about.

October 10, 1492, First Voyage
The crew is terrified. They are too far out in the ocean. Some believe sea monsters will eat them. Food and water are low. No land is in sight. Sailors threaten to seize the ship and return home. What could Columbus say to calm their fears?

_____

_____

_____

June 29, 1502, Fourth Voyage
The new governor of Santo Domingo, Nicolás de Ovando, does not want Columbus around. Years later, Columbus is shipwrecked. He must ask the hostile governor for help. What might Columbus say to him?

_____

_____

_____

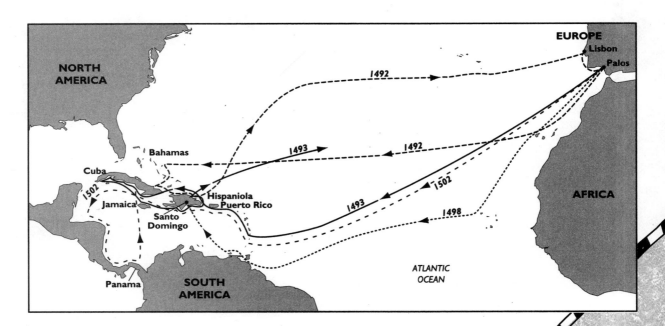

**Columbus's Voyages to the New World,
1492, 1493, 1498, and 1502**

Travel Light

The goal of Columbus's second voyage was to build a colony. What do colonists need to survive? What won't they find in the New World? Cross out five items that you think Columbus should not take. Explain the reasons for your choices.

SHIP'S STOCK

Building Tools

Warm Clothes

Firewood

Trinkets (beads, for example)

Lumber for Houses

Oil Lamps

Furniture

Pots and Pans

Horses

Cows

Sheep

Goats

Compass

Blankets

Jewelry

Mixed-Up Misnomer

Have you ever wondered how Native Americans came to be called Indians? (After all, that's what the people of India are called.) The use of the term *Indians* to describe Native Americans is an example of a true misnomer, a name that does not fit. It was the result of Columbus's mistaken sense of the world.

Columbus had wanted to be the first to find a route from Europe to the Indies. (The name *Indies* is what people called Southeast Asia, India, and Indochina in those years). Like everyone else at that time, Columbus did not know that North and South America lay right smack in his way!

When Columbus landed on an island in the Bahamas, he was sure that he was someplace in the Indies. That is why he called the inhabitants of the island Indians. That is why, too, that the islands off the east coast of America are known today as the West Indies.

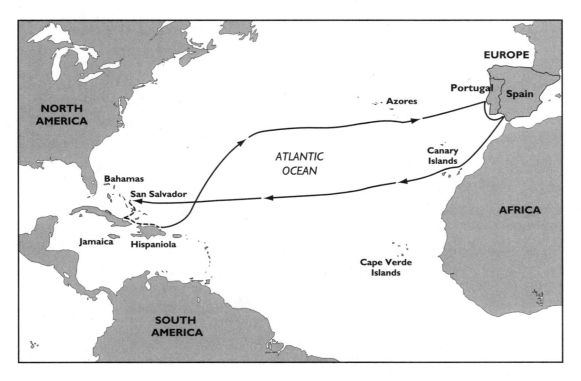

Columbus's Voyage of 1492

John Cabot
(1450?–1498?)

Christopher Columbus and John Cabot never met. Yet their lives ran parallel, like sprinters on a track. They both came from Genoa, Italy. They were about the same age. And they shared the same dream: sailing west to Asia. Cabot was a spice trader in Venice, Italy. Getting spices from the Far East was tough and slow. Hostile armies and high mountains stood in the way. So merchants sailed the long way around Africa. Like many traders, Cabot dreamed of a better route.

Years later, in 1493, Cabot was living in England. News arrived: Columbus had sailed across the Atlantic Ocean to "Asia" (really America)! Cabot thought he knew a faster route—across the *North* Atlantic. With one eye on future "Asian" riches, King Henry VII of England paid for Cabot's voyage.

In May 1497, Cabot and 18 men set sail. A month later, Cabot spotted "Asia" (probably Newfoundland or Nova Scotia, Canada). Cabot claimed the land for England—that country's first piece of the New World. Like Columbus, Cabot thought "Asian" riches would soon be his. But his richest find was a prime fishing area now called the Grand Banks.

In 1498, Cabot set sail again with five ships. The trip was pure disaster. A storm forced one ship back to England. The others, Cabot's included, never returned.

In 1508, Cabot's son, Sebastian, tried to find a route to Asia. He was the first of many explorers to seek a northwest passage across Canada. The passage wasn't found until 1853, 345 years later.

The Northeast Coast, 1497 and 1498

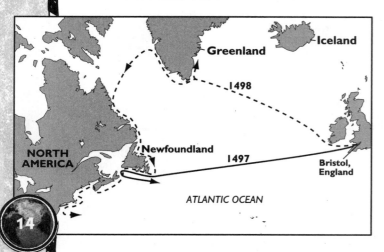

Risky Business

On his first voyage, John Cabot risked his life. On the second, he lost it.
Are explorers reckless and foolish? Or daring and brave? Read about
Cabot's rewards. Then explain if and when you would risk your life
for each one.

1. When (if at all) is WEALTH worth risking your life for?

   Instead of Asian riches, Cabot found "infinite fish: sturgeons, salmon,
   very large soles a yard in length." Other explorers did become wealthy.

   For WEALTH, I would _____

   _____

   _____

2. When (if at all) is FAME worth risking your life for?

   An Italian wrote: "[Cabot] is called the Great Admiral. Vast honor is
   paid to him. The English run after him like mad." Other explorers
   were forgotten.

   For FAME, I would _____

   _____

   _____

3. When (if at all) is ADVENTURE worth risking your life for?

   Seeing the New World for the first time was different and exciting.
   But sailors also endured weeks of boring ocean.

   For ADVENTURE, I would _____

   _____

   _____

CABOT'S CREW

Cabot's crew earned a wage, but no fame and glory. Pretend Cabot
asked you to join his crew. Accept or reject his offer in a letter.
Explain your reasons. (You can write on the back of this page.)

Juan Ponce de León
(1474–1521)

MAJOR ACHIEVEMENT:
He was the first European to explore Florida.

Juan Ponce de León had sailed with Columbus on his second voyage. Later he started and ruled a colony on Puerto Rico ("rich port" in Spanish). The island's gold made Ponce de León one of the richest men in the New World.

Money was no stranger to Ponce de León. He grew up in a noble family in Spain. He had even trained to be a knight. But in 1511, Juan Ponce de León was a man without a command. He lost his governor's title to Christopher Columbus's son, Diego. King Ferdinand offered Ponce de León an unexplored island named Bimini. If he could find it, the king promised, he could rule it.

One myth says that Ponce de León set off in search of the Fountain of Youth. The fountain magically made old people young. But how many explorers really believed this? Probably not many.

The real story is much more ordinary. Ponce de León set sail to Bimini to find gold, power, and fame. On the way, he spotted a land "full of flowers"—*La Florida* in Spanish. The loyal explorer claimed La Florida for Spain. Then he sailed along the coasts and into the Gulf of Mexico.

Landings were short and tense. Native people fought to keep strangers away. Even so, Ponce de León looked for a place to put a colony. Indians attacked in force. Injured, Ponce de León and a few survivors retreated. The so-called Fountain of Youth explorer died of his wound, never even growing old.

Florida, 1513

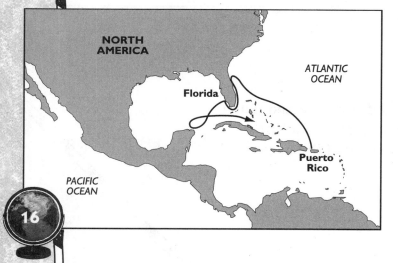

Just Your Imagination

Finding the Fountain of Youth was an empty dream for some explorers.
But just imagine that Ponce de León had found a fountain that made
old people young.

**What are all the good things
about having a Fountain
of Youth?**

**What are all the bad things
about having a Fountain
of Youth?**

_____   _____

_____   _____

_____   _____

_____   _____

_____   _____

_____   _____

_____   _____

_____   _____

_____   _____

_____   _____

How would finding the Fountain of Youth have changed history?
What would the state of Florida be like?

_____

_____

_____

_____

Hernando Cortez
(1485–1547)

At age 14, Hernando Cortez left his family to study law. The life of a lawyer would have been cozy. But to Cortez, it was just plain dull. He had adventure in his blood. Cortez quit school and later sailed to the New World. He joined his fellow Spaniards in Cuba.

By this time, most of the Caribbean islands were under firm Spanish rule. Soldiers had murdered, starved, or driven out the native people. But the biggest killer was the tiniest one. The smallpox virus from Europe had wiped out entire native populations.

In 1519, Cortez led an army to Mexico—a land firmly ruled by Indians. The goal was to steal riches from the Aztecs. The Aztec cities were large and advanced. Montezuma, the leader, heard that Cortez was coming. To avoid war, Montezuma tried to buy off the army with gold, silver, and gems. An Aztec woman named Marinche even joined the Spaniards. Montezuma's plan backfired. To Cortez, the gifts simply meant that the Aztecs had plenty of riches to plunder.

Cortez's army attacked, but Aztecs killed half the men. In Cuba, Cortez amassed a bigger army. Marinche spoke the Nahuatl and Maya Indian languages. So she became Cortez's interpreter. She taught Cortez about Aztec customs. The second army landed in Mexico. The deadly smallpox virus had already found its way to the mainland. Aztecs began to get sick and die. Cortez took the Aztec capital. Soldiers looted the city, including Montezuma's house, for gold.

Cortez later explored Central America and lower California. His reward? A noble title and 23,000 enslaved Indians.

Mexico and Central America, 1519–1521
Southern California, 1535

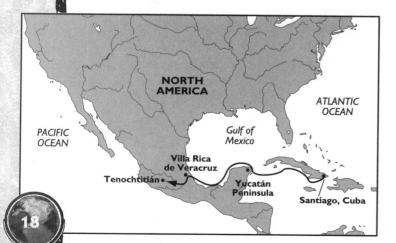

Place Names

Spanish explorers gave Spanish names to the places they claimed or conquered. You are probably so familiar with these names that you don't even realize they're Spanish. Try to match the Spanish names below with their English meanings. Hint: Most sound like their English counterparts. Use a Spanish dictionary, if you like.

Name of Place	Meaning
_____ 1. Florida	**A.** Beautiful View
_____ 2. Colorado	**B.** Salt Mines
_____ 3. Montana	**C.** The Pass
_____ 4. Mesa (Arizona)	**D.** Plateau (literally "table")
_____ 5. Los Angeles (California)	**E.** Land of Flowers
_____ 6. Buena Vista (California)	**F.** Cask
_____ 7. Salinas (California)	**G.** The Angels
_____ 8. El Paso (Texas)	**H.** Yellow
_____ 9. Amarillo (Texas)	**I.** Mountain
_____ 10. Cuba	**J.** Red

Hola

¿Cómo estás?

Bien y tú

Gracias

Adiós

ÉSTADOS UNIDOS (United States)

On a map of the United States, look for more Spanish names. In what part of the country do most Spanish names appear? Why?

_____

_____

_____

_____

_____

_____

_____

Giovanni Verrazano
(1485?–1528)

When cultures meet, anything can happen. And Giovanni Verrazano met with many cultures on his voyages. He described the people he met in great detail, providing nontraveling Europeans with a clear picture of what cultures in the New World were like.

King Francis I, Verrazano's sponsor, had other goals for him. He hoped Verrazano would be the lucky one to find a sea route to China. He also wanted New World riches.

In 1524, Verrazano sailed west and landed in what is now North Carolina. He gave French names to everything he saw to honor the king, but few names survived. Verrazano then stopped at present-day New York Bay, Narragansett Bay, and Newfoundland. At each stop he met different cultures. The only common ground was fear. Native Americans ran from the white men. Europeans were cautious about going ashore. Yet each meeting helped to melt the fear.

At one stop a sailor swam ashore to offer trifles (paper, glass, bells, and so on). Fearful, he quickly tossed the trinkets on land and swam back. The current was too strong. Indians saved his life. When the sailor woke up, he screamed in fear of his rescuers. To calm him, the Indians warmed him by the fire. As the sailor gained strength, he nervously asked to leave. "With great love," wrote Verrazano, "the Indians helped return him to the ship safely."

On his last voyage, Verrazano met the Caribs—fierce people who warred with the peaceful Arawaks. But by this time, Spaniards were wiping out Arawaks and Caribs alike through disease, slavery, and war. The Caribs killed and ate Verrazano. The crew didn't get to China. But they took the king a hull full of wood from Brazil.

North Carolina to Newfoundland, 1524
Brazil, 1527
Caribbean, 1528

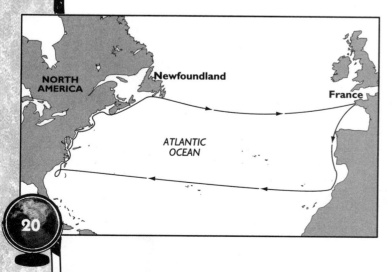

NORTH AMERICA

Newfoundland

France

ATLANTIC OCEAN

First Encounters

Giovanni Verrazano described the Native Americans he first encountered. They appeared different from people he'd known before. However, Verrazano and his sailors probably appeared odd to the Native Americans, too. Read the excerpt from Giovanni Verrazano's journal. Then imagine that you are a Native American seeing an explorer for the first time. Describe for others the oddity of these men.

These people [wear] a narrow girdle of grass, hanged about with tails of beasts . . . dangling down to their knees. Some wear garlands of feathers. The people are of colour russet . . . their hair black, thick, and not very long, which they tie in a knot and wear like a tail. They are of medium stature, broad-breasted, strong arms, their bodies well-fashioned . . . Many of them have black and great eyes with a cheerful and steady look, sharp-witted, nimble, and great runners.

—Giovanni Verrazano

Hernando de Soto
(1496?–1542)

MAJOR ACHIEVEMENT:

De Soto was the first European to find the Mississippi River.

Hernando de Soto was rich. But he wanted to get richer. So he got permission from the king of Spain to go on a treasure hunt. He was looking for New World gold. And he planned to find it in Florida.

In 1539, de Soto, 600 soldiers, and 100 servants landed in Tampa Bay, Florida. Juan Ponce de León had explored only the coast. So de Soto marched inland through tangled forests and swamps. Within months, food was low. No gold was in sight. The crew wanted to turn back, but they kept going. They plodded along the Savannah River in Georgia to the Blue Ridge Mountains. They crossed the mountains to the Alabama River.

In Mobile, Alabama, de Soto lost men, horses, and pigs in a battle with Indians. Food and ammunition were more limited. Clothes wore out. There was no medicine. The men pressed on, exploring Alabama and Mississippi. Near Quizquiz (Memphis, Tennessee), a scout left to look for corn. After a few days, he stepped out of a forest. Before him was the mighty Mississippi, the biggest river in the United States. The explorers wandered around Arkansas and then returned. At the Mississippi River, de Soto died of a fever. His men continued to explore as far west as present-day Texas.

At first, people ignored de Soto's three-year journey. They said he treated Indians poorly and was greedy. But the discovery of a river as great as the Mississippi was too important to ignore. The river gave future explorers their first access into the untamed heart of America.

Mississippi River and Southern States, 1539–1542

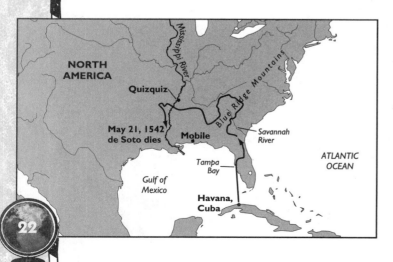

What's Your Opinion?

What do you think about de Soto and other early explorers? Were they brave men who risked their lives to explore? Or were they greedy murderers? Complete each phrase below. First circle *were* or *were not*. Then write the reason.

De Soto and other explorers of the sixteenth century

were/were not **brave** because _____

_____

were/were not **kind** because _____

_____

were/were not **violent** because _____

_____

were/were not **greedy** because _____

_____

were/were not **loyal** because _____

_____

were/were not **heroes** because _____

_____

Tell about a goal that is important to you. How do you describe the way you work toward your goal? How do others see you? _____

_____

_____

_____

_____

_____

_____

_____

What's So Hot About Spices?

**Would you go halfway around the world for pepper?
You might if you had to eat rotten meat!**

Before refrigeration, people preserved food by drowning it in salt. This might have preserved it for a time, but salted meat tasted like salt. What's more, the meat spoiled quickly anyway. And because people couldn't afford to throw it away, they ate the meat—rotten or not.

There was one solution: pepper. But only one way existed to obtain pepper—from the Arab traders of the Middle East. They sold goods found in India and the Far East, like silk, carpets, jewelry, and such spices as cloves, nutmeg, ginger, and—best of all—pepper. Europeans came to depend on these spices. However, war with the Middle East halted their supply.

The Italian ports of Venice and Genoa offered new hope when Italian explorer Marco Polo found the source of all these goods. Europeans came to depend less and less on Middle Eastern merchants, traveling to get the spices themselves. Even though they faced enemies of war, pirates, rough terrain, and dangerous seas, the risk was worth it. Today a box of pepper costs just a dollar or two. But back then a modest pile of peppercorns could buy a house!

Portuguese traders soon found a new route, though, which bypassed Venice and Genoa. The Italians faced a bleak future. Many dreamed of a western route to Asia. Columbus, Cabot, and other explorers from Venice and Genoa put their dreams into action. They decided to sail halfway around the world—in search of pepper!

Think about something you depend on today. What if you suddenly couldn't get it? Would you travel around the world to find it? Explain your answer. (You can write on the back of this page.)

Part 2

They Navigated the Great Rivers and Lakes

Early explorers had no planes, trains, or automobiles. Sailing was the way to go. Sea captains in the New World charted many bays, rivers, and lakes. These waterways took waves of explorers deeper inland. More Europeans claimed Indian homelands. Native people grew hostile. Clashes between the cultures became frequent and violent.

BIG QUESTIONS

- In what ways are cultures different?
- How can differences lead to conflict?
- How can people speaking different languages communicate?

Jacques Cartier
(1491–1557)

Columbus was Italian but sailed for Spain. Cabot was Italian but sailed for England. Verrazano, also Italian, sailed for France. The seamen of Italy's great trading ports, Venice and Genoa, were among the best. But monarchs also looked to their own subjects. In 1534, Verrazano's sponsor, King Francis I of France, put his money on Jacques Cartier, a Frenchman.

Cartier's orders were familiar: find a northwest passage to China. He probed the coast of Canada for an opening —any opening. In and out of bays, inlets, and sounds, he hit dead ends. Finally, Cartier sailed an icy strait to the Gulf of St. Lawrence and *la Grande Rivière*, the "Big River." He claimed the region for France and sailed home. On board were two young Indian boys.

A year later, Cartier picked up where he had left off. He camped at the mouth of the St. Lawrence River. The two Indian boys told Cartier about a city of gold and gems upstream. What explorer could resist? Cartier sailed to Indian villages near Quebec and Montreal. Instead of gold, he found another dead end. By climbing Mont Réal (Mount Royal), Cartier saw that dangerous rapids blocked the route west.

The explorers spent a harsh winter in agony. Despite help from Indians, many sailors died of scurvy and other diseases. In May, Cartier brought more Indians on board, including Chief Donnacona. Then he headed home.

On Cartier's last voyage, the French and the Indians grew hostile. The first French colony failed to take hold. But others would soon succeed. Cartier's river opened inland North America to France. And France took full advantage.

**St. Lawrence River,
1534, 1535, 1541**

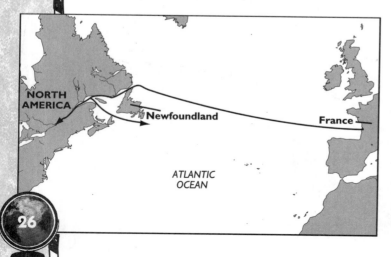

Upstream, Downstream

The first explorers to an area didn't have maps. They used geography, science, and common sense to navigate unknown waters. Read each fact. Then circle the letter of the correct answer.

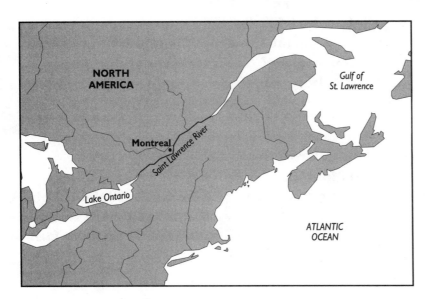

1. The ocean is at sea level, which is usually lower than the land. Therefore, the St. Lawrence River flows

   (a) in from the ocean   (b) out to the ocean   (c) both ways

2. The Great Lakes have fresh water. Ocean water is salty. The St. Lawrence River is

   (a) fresh   (b) salty   (c) in between ocean water and fresh water

3. Rivers form because water on higher ground has to flow downward. It's the law of gravity. The water in the St. Lawrence River came from

   (a) the Great Lakes   (b) the ocean   (c) both

4. Rain adds water to a river, making it rise. Suppose the river doesn't overflow. After a big rain, the river

   (a) flows the same   (b) slows down   (c) speeds up

WATERSHED

Is there a river near your town? Do you know where it starts? Use a local map to trace the source upstream. Remember: Rivers always go from higher ground to lower ground. It's the law of gravity!

27

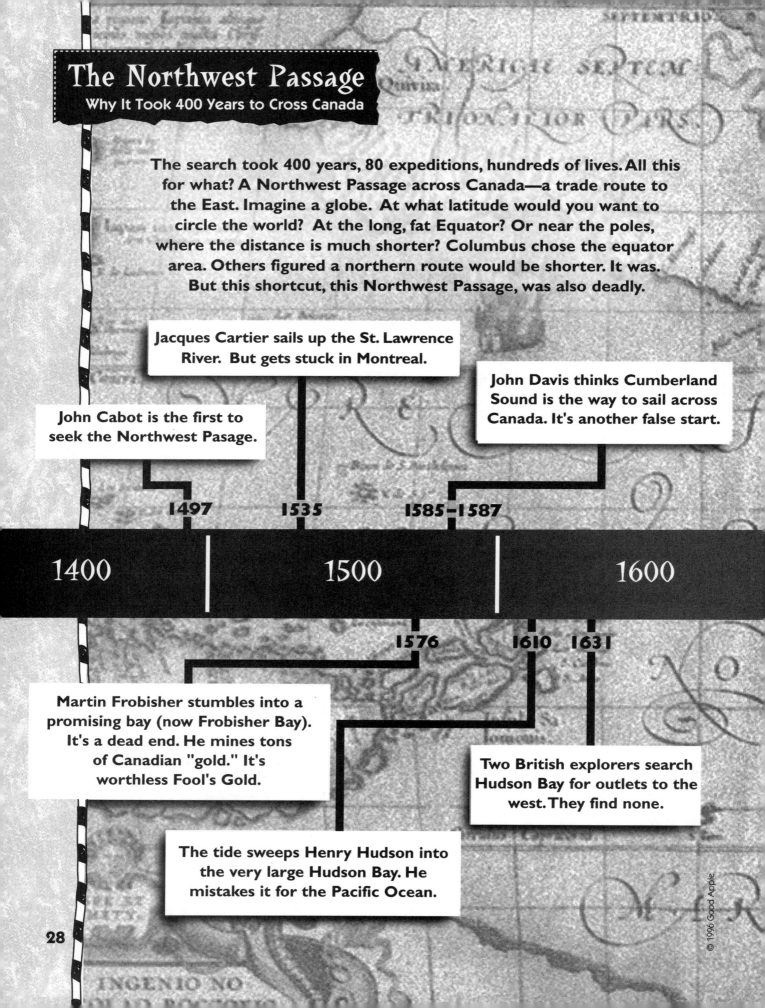

The Northwest Passage
Why It Took 400 Years to Cross Canada

The search took 400 years, 80 expeditions, hundreds of lives. All this for what? A Northwest Passage across Canada—a trade route to the East. Imagine a globe. At what latitude would you want to circle the world? At the long, fat Equator? Or near the poles, where the distance is much shorter? Columbus chose the equator area. Others figured a northern route would be shorter. It was. But this shortcut, this Northwest Passage, was also deadly.

Jacques Cartier sails up the St. Lawrence River. But gets stuck in Montreal.

John Davis thinks Cumberland Sound is the way to sail across Canada. It's another false start.

John Cabot is the first to seek the Northwest Pasage.

1497   **1535**   **1585–1587**

1400   **1500**   **1600**

1576   **1610**   **1631**

Martin Frobisher stumbles into a promising bay (now Frobisher Bay). It's a dead end. He mines tons of Canadian "gold." It's worthless Fool's Gold.

Two British explorers search Hudson Bay for outlets to the west. They find none.

The tide sweeps Henry Hudson into the very large Hudson Bay. He mistakes it for the Pacific Ocean.

28

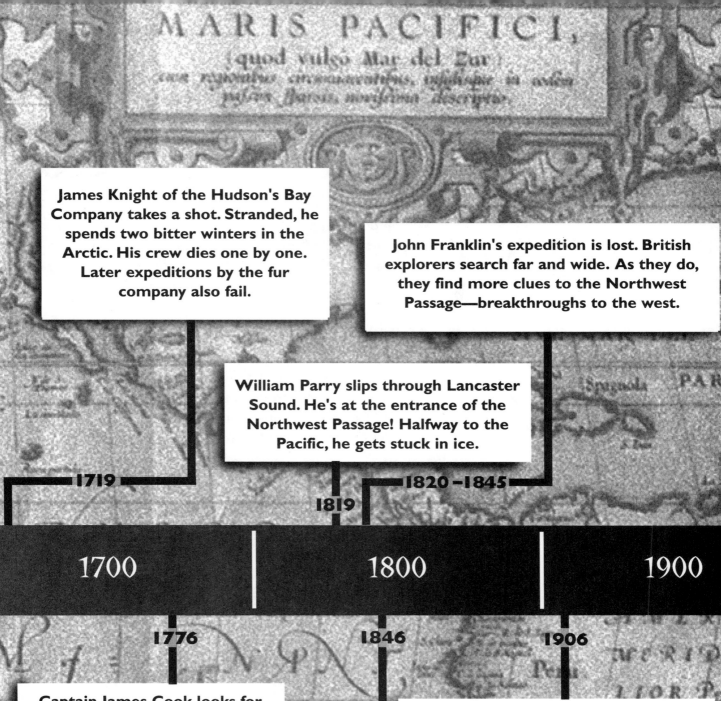

MARIS PACIFICI,
(quod vulgo Mar del Zur)

James Knight of the Hudson's Bay Company takes a shot. Stranded, he spends two bitter winters in the Arctic. His crew dies one by one. Later expeditions by the fur company also fail.

John Franklin's expedition is lost. British explorers search far and wide. As they do, they find more clues to the Northwest Passage—breakthroughs to the west.

William Parry slips through Lancaster Sound. He's at the entrance of the Northwest Passage! Halfway to the Pacific, he gets stuck in ice.

1719

1820–1845

1819

1700   **1800**   **1900**

1776

1846

1906

Captain James Cook looks for the passage from the other end. He scouts the Pacific shoreline of Alaska with no luck.

Raold Amundsen is the first to navigate the whole Northwest Passage. But now, the world doesn't need it. Trade routes to Asia are plentiful. Airplanes will soon make an Arctic shipping lane useless.

Many explorers fail to sail the Northwest Passage. Ice is thick. The route winds in and out.

Samuel de Champlain
(1570?-1635)

MAJOR ACHIEVEMENT:

Champlain founded the first French settlement in the New World—the city of Quebec.

Samuel de Champlain was a sea captain's son. So to no one's surprise, he became a seaman. Champlain sailed to the West Indies, Mexico, and Panama. These areas were well settled, mostly by the Spanish. King Henry IV of France wanted New World land for France. He asked Champlain to get it.

In 1603, Samuel de Champlain explored the St. Lawrence River, as Jacques Cartier had done. But unlike Cartier, he went past the rapids to the west. Champlain saw the roaring Niagara Falls, Great Lakes Huron and Ontario, and Lake Champlain in New York.

Following the king's orders, Champlain put up a trading post, a fort, and a storehouse. He called the new town Quebec. The explorers spent their first bitter-cold winter there. Only 8 of the 20 settlers survived. In later years the death toll improved as the French grew used to the climate.

Between 1610 and 1624, Champlain bounced between France and Quebec. Then in 1626, England stormed the settlement. France and England were at war. The English ordered everyone to surrender. The French held out for a year. But they ran out of food. The English captured Champlain and took their prisoner to England. They later let him go. Quebec was destroyed in the conflict.

In 1632 a treaty (agreement) between France and England ended the war. In it, England agreed to give Quebec back to France. Champlain sailed to Canada, rebuilt the fort, and lived there until his death.

St. Lawrence River and Great Lakes Region, 1603–1615

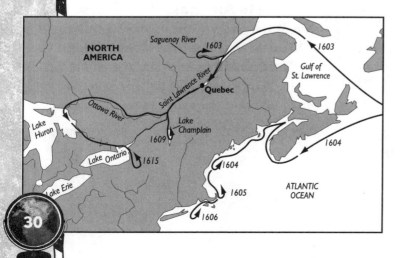

30

Hello, Hello

Samuel de Champlain made friends with many
people from different cultures. Pretend you're
on a ship. You must gather food and supplies
on land. Native people group together on
shore. How do you let them know you're
friendly? How do you earn their trust? How
do you convince them to let you stay?
Explain your strategy in each case below.

The people run away at the first sight of you. _____

_____

_____

The people attack as soon as you set foot ashore. _____

_____

_____

_____

The people offer you gifts and food but tell you to leave. _____

_____

_____

_____

The people wait for you to make the first move. They are ready to run

or attack. _____

_____

_____

_____

_____

Henry Hudson
(?–1611)

An explorer could starve to death. Illness or injury could kill him or her. Bad weather or icebergs could wreck the ship. On top of all that, explorers faced another danger: their own crew. Seamen worked a ship for a wage. When the going got too rough, some cried "Mutiny!" They took over the ship. That was Henry Hudson's sad fate. He died adrift in a small boat in the bay that bears his name.

Henry Hudson's birthday and his birthplace in England are not known. Companies, not just kings and queens, paid explorers to explore. They hoped to profit from new trading routes and sources of goods. Hudson made four such voyages to find a northwest passage across Canada.

On the third voyage he sailed up the present-day Hudson River for a Dutch company. But he hit a dead end. The next year, he sailed into what today is called Hudson Bay for English merchants. This huge body of water, thought Hudson, must go to the Pacific Ocean. But when he tried to sail west, he struck out again.

Henry Hudson and crew wintered in the bay. Arctic winters are dark most of the time and bitter cold all of the time. Food is nearly impossible to find. The crew boiled over in anger. They took the ship. Then they put Hudson, his son John, and seven men in a small boat. They had no supplies—and no chance to survive. Only the name lived on: Hudson Bay, Hudson Strait, Hudson River, and two Hudson towns.

New York and parts of Canada, 1607–1610

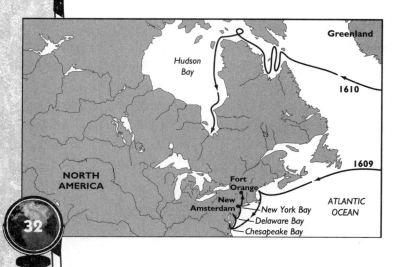

Afloat in a Boat

Imagine that you are in the boat with Henry Hudson and the others. The mutineers offer you eight items from the ship. Circle your choices on the list below. Then explain the reasons for your choices.

Star Map	**First Aid Kit**	**Fishing Net**
Salt	**Compass**	**Butter**
Blankets	**Biscuits**	**Lemon Juice**
Coffee	**Drinking Water**	**Oil Lamp (and oil)**

_____
_____
_____
_____
_____
_____
_____
_____
_____
_____
_____
_____
_____

Robert de La Salle
(Rene-Robert Cavalier)
(1643–1687)

Spain, Britain, France, and Holland competed for the best land in America. In an era of sailing ships, good land meant good waterways. France had already grabbed the St. Lawrence River. Thanks to Robert de La Salle, France took the Mississippi River, too.

From 1669 to 1673, La Salle wandered around the Great Lakes region. So much water! So many resources! He went up the St. Lawrence, around the tip of lower Michigan, and down Lake Michigan. He knew a great trading route when he saw it. On the Illinois River, La Salle built forts. But Iroquois tribes called the area home. They drove out the French.

La Salle went back to exploring. In 1682 he sailed the Mississippi River. At each bend he grew more excited. The land was rich and ripe for settlers. Best of all, the river could carry those settlers to and from the Gulf of Mexico. At the river's mouth, La Salle shouted, "In the name of Louis, the Great King of France, I take possession of this country." In honor of King Louis, he named it Louisiana.

La Salle's Louisiana included all the sources of water that drained into the Mississippi. It stretched from the Appalachian Mountains in the east to the Rocky Mountains in the west and from the Great Lakes in the north to the Gulf of Mexico in the south.

La Salle later tried to set up a colony. But he got lost and landed in Texas. The settlers failed three times to reach the Mississippi by land. Frustrated, they shot La Salle. He was buried in the rich, ripe region that he admired.

Mississippi River Valley, 1682

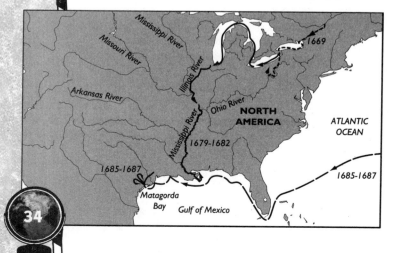

The Mighty Mississippi

La Salle found the mouth of the Mississippi River near New Orleans, Louisiana. Can you find the source? On the map below, follow the river upstream. Note that Baton Rouge, Louisiana, is one city on the Mississippi. Write the names of nine other cities on the Mississippi. Then answer the questions that follow.

1. Baton Rouge, Louisiana

2. _____

3. _____

4. _____

5. _____

6. _____

7. _____

8. _____

9. _____

10. _____

What are the state and nearest city at the river's source? _____

How many states border the Mississippi? _____

How many state capitals do? _____

FLOOD PLAIN

In the early 1990s the Mississippi flooded nearby cities. People lost their lives and their homes. Why do you think many people still live on the riverbank? Would you? Explain your answer.

_____

_____

_____

_____

Sieur de Bienville
(Jean Baptiste Le Moyne)
(1680–1768)

Two brothers—Jean Baptiste Le Moyne, Sieur de Bienville, and Pierre Le Moyne, Sieur d'Iberville—picked up where Robert de La Salle had left off. La Salle claimed Louisiana for France. But he failed to settle it. Without settlements, land claims were all but worthless.

Bienville and his brother Iberville were settlers themselves. They came from a family of 11 boys and three girls in Montreal, Canada. All colonies were in constant danger of takeover. The French, British, and Spanish battled hard for land. One took a fort, and the other took it back.

Iberville fought the British in northern Canada. At age 12, Bienville joined his older brother. Years later, Iberville turned to exploration. Bienville, now grown, tagged along again.

In 1699 the brothers reached the mouth of the Mississippi River. They founded a town near Biloxi, Mississippi—France's first toehold in the area. They built a post near New Orleans, Louisiana—a second toehold. Iberville was called to fight the British again. But this time, Bienville didn't follow. Instead, he explored Louisiana. He learned about the land and the native people who had lived there for centuries.

As the new governor, Bienville quickly set up Fort Mobile—now Mobile, Alabama. But yellow fever wiped out too many settlers. Bienville lost his title. Later he fought the Natchez Indians and won. He built a fort in what is now Natchez, Mississippi. Once again made governor, Bienville founded New Orleans. After he retired, Spain took Bienville's colony from France.

Louisiana Province, 1700–1739

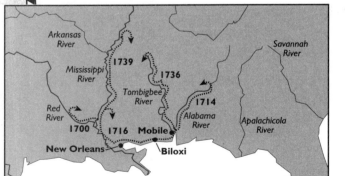

Parlez-Vous Français?
("Do you speak French?")

French explorers used their language to name the new land. Many French words sound like the same words in English. How many place names can you match? Use a French dictionary if you like.

Bonjour

Ça va?

Name of Place **English Meaning**

_____ **I.** Montréal (Canada)   **A.** Of the Monks

_____ **2.** Detroit (Michigan)   **B.** High Land

_____ **3.** Louisville (Kentucky)   **C.** The Cross

_____ **4.** Trois Rivières (Canada) **D.** Red Stick (or baton)

_____ **5.** Montpelier (Vermont)   **E.** Royal Mountain

_____ **6.** Baton Rouge (Louisiana) **F.** Pelier Mountain

_____ **7.** Terre Haute (Indiana)   **G.** Clear Water

_____ **8.** La Crosse (Wisconsin)   **H.** Three Rivers

_____ **9.** Eau Claire (Wisconsin)   **I.** Strait

_____ **10.** Des Moines (Iowa)   **J.** Town of (King) Louis

Trés bien

Merci

Au revoir

ÉTATS-UNIS (United States)

On a map of the United States, look for more French names. In what part of the country do most French names appear? Why?

_____

_____

_____

_____

_____

_____

_____

Limey Lifesavers

Do you know why British sailors are called *limeys*? It's short for "lime-juicer." In the 1890s British law required sailors to drink lime juice each day. Doctors had just discovered that the juice is a lifesaver. It prevents a deadly disease called scurvy.

In winter, many of the crew where attacked by a certain maladay called the scurvy. Scarcely anything but liquid could be eaten. There teeth became very loose. They could be pulled out with the fingers without causing pain.

A violent pain seized their arms and legs. The limbs remained swollen and hard and spotted, as of with flea-bites. They could not walk.

They were without strength and suffered great pains. They had a very bad cough and short breath.

Later, doctors learned that the vitamin C in the juice is the real lifesaver. Today, vitamin C is plentiful and scurvy is rare. But before people knew the cause, scurvy killed millions. Easy victims were sailors on long sea voyages. People in cold climates suffered, too. They had fewer sources of vitamin C.

Explorers on long sea voyages to northern climates were hit doubly hard. Jacques Cartier lost 110 men to the disease. Samuel de Champlain lost nearly 8 out of 10 men in his crew. He described scurvy in 1609.

Think about something else that people didn't have in the 1800s that we have today. It can be an invention, a medical cure, or anything else. Write about it, explaining how it makes our lives better.

Part 3

They Crossed Great Plains and Deserts

French and British explorers had opened the watery northeast. Spanish explorers in the south pushed north and west. They crossed wide, flat plains and hot, stark deserts. Slowly the vast size of this country became clear. The race began to explore it all.

BIG QUESTIONS

- As explorers pushed inland, how did relations with Native Americans improve?

- How did they worsen?

- Why wasn't America big enough for everyone?

Estevanico
(Little Stephen)
(?–1539)

The first African to reach America sailed with Christopher Columbus. His name was Pedro Niño. Other explorers brought Africans to the New World, too. The most famous was Estevanico, a slave from Morocco, North Africa. His owner was an unlucky Spanish explorer named Pánfilo de Narváez.

Narváez set sail for the New World with hundreds of men. Only four survived. In Santo Domingo, 143 men deserted. Near Cuba a hurricane swept away more men. It blew the ships off course. Instead of landing in Texas, the explorers landed near Tampa, Florida. Forty more men died of hunger and disease. Stranded, the crew tried to build boats. But the vessels sank or crashed.

Indians captured the only four survivors. Estevanico was one of them. He had learned medicine from Arabs. So he showed that his hands had healing powers. The Indians let the prisoners live. Estevanico soon learned their language and customs. He also learned of the Seven Cities of Cíbola, each made of gold.

After escaping, the explorers walked hundreds of miles. They looked in vain for golden cities. Eight years later the party reached a Spanish colony near the Gulf of California in Mexico. The governor hired Estevanico and others to find the golden cities. Estevanico scouted ahead for good routes. He made contact with native people. To protect against attack, he wore the colorful feathers and bells of a medicine man. Through Arizona and into New Mexico, Estevanico thought he had found the Seven Cities of Cíbola. But it was a simple Zuni Indian village. The Zunis killed Estevanico as a spy. But the quest for golden cities lived on.

Arizona and New Mexico, 1539

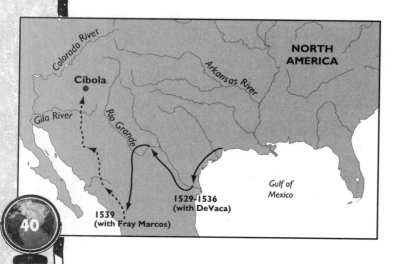

Dear Diary

How would you feel in Estevanico's shoes? Finish each diary entry.

1. I am sailing to the New World for the first time. I look forward to

   _____

   but I fear _____

2. Near Cuba a hurricane hit our ship. It felt like _____

   I heard _____

   I saw _____

3. After seven years of walking across America, we survive by _____

   _____

   and by _____

   _____

4. I have found the Seven Cities of Cíbola. But the Zunis think I am a spy.

   I must earn their trust by _____

   _____

   and also by _____

5. My greatest fear is _____

   _____

6. My greatest wish is _____

   _____

Francisco Vasquez de Coronado
(1510–1554)

The Southwest, 1540–1542

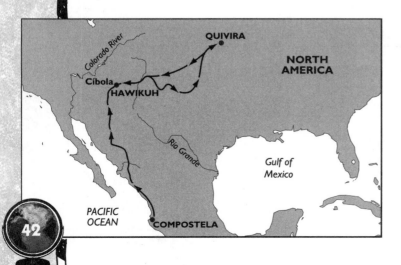

MAJOR ACHIEVEMENT:

Coronado claimed Arizona, Oklahoma, and Kansas for Spain. He strengthened Spain's claim in Texas and New Mexico.

In the sixteenth century, gold was like a magnet. Gold pulled men across oceans, over mountains, and through deserts. So imagine the governor of Mexico's reaction to this news: A whole city made of gold! Roofs lined with jewels! And proof! A Spaniard named Fray Marcos said he had seen it.

Marcos had returned from an expedition to look for the Seven Cities of Cíbola. Estevanico, the scout, had clearly reached these golden cities. But he was killed by Zuni Indians. Marcos himself had seen Cíbola from afar. He saw sparkling jewels and gold houses—just as the stories said.

In 1540 the governor put Francisco Coronado on the trail. Fray Marcos pointed the way. The army crossed the Arizona desert. They stopped at the first village. The walls were sunbaked clay, not gold. They were dotted with stones, not jewels. The villagers pointed north. Coronado crossed New Mexico, Texas, Oklahoma, and Kansas. Still no cities of gold. Just Indian villages of Hopis, Zunis, Quiviras (Wichitas), and others.

Fray Marcos admitted he had led everyone astray. After two years of searching, Coronado was empty-handed. But the trip wasn't worthless. The payoff was land. Coronado expanded Spain's empire. He extended the frontiers— the borders between the explored and the unexplored. He showed how very, very wide this land stretched.

A Beast to Remember

Coronado met many strange animals. He couldn't take photos to show the Europeans at home. So he described the animals in words. Can you guess what "foul beast" Coronado has just met? Can you draw it?

Their faces are short and narrow between the eyes. Their eyes bulge on the sides so that, when they run, they can see those who follow. They are bearded like very large goats. When they run, their beards touch the ground.

From the middle of the body back, they are covered with very woolly hair like that of a sheep.

From belly to front, they have very heavy hair like the mane of a lion. They have a hump larger than that of a camel. Their horns are short and heavy.

They have short tails with a clump of hair on the end. When they run, they carry their tails up like a scorpion.

It is a foul beast in manner and form of body.

My guess: _____

My reasons: _____

_____

THE ANIMAL GAME

Describe an animal aloud without naming it. Who can guess it first?

Daniel Boone
(1734–1820)

In the eighteenth century, people usually didn't live beyond the age of 40. Explorers often lived less than that. They took risks and faced hazards. But Daniel Boone beat all the odds. He lived 85 rugged years. Stories of how he escaped death at every bend became legend.

Boone was a pioneer, spy, soldier, trailblazer, hunter, and founder of colonies. He thrived on the American frontier. At the time, that frontier was Kentucky. Boone cleared a trail out there from Virginia. His "Wilderness Road" took thousands of settlers west.

Boone grew up in Pennsylvania and North Carolina. His parents owned two farms, a blacksmith shop, and a weaving shop. The 11 Boone children didn't go to school much. But Daniel Boone learned to read and write.

At age 12, Boone got his first rifle and named it Tick-Licker. He became a skilled hunter and even supplied the family's food. At age 20, Boone joined the British army. There he heard about the rich land and plentiful animals in Kentucky. Later he went to explore.

Sure enough, the land was full of deer, turkeys, and buffaloes. But it was also full of danger. In two years, Native Americans captured Boone several times. They tortured and killed his son. They stole his furs. Boone built a fort called Boonesborough. Settlers at the fort suffered more attacks. Again, Boone was captured. Shawnees made him a brave and called him Shel-tow-ee (Big Turtle). But again, Boone escaped. He went to defend the Boonesborough settlers. In his later years, Boone's eyesight grew poor. But he kept his frontier lifestyle. He spent his last years exploring farther west. That's where the American frontier was rapidly rolling.

Appalachian Mountains and Kentucky, 1767–1769

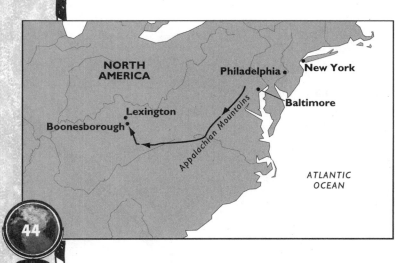

Westward Ho!

Pioneers such as Daniel Boone had different reasons for moving west. The wilderness was rugged and dangerous. So the reasons must have been very good. Explain what you think each person below hoped to find.

1. A trapper or hunter: _____
_____
_____
_____
_____

2. A farmer: _____
_____
_____
_____
_____

3. A blacksmith: _____
_____
_____
_____
_____

4. A settler: _____
_____
_____
_____
_____

5. A Native American: _____
_____
_____
_____

6. A slave: _____
_____
_____
_____

7. A free African American: _____
_____
_____
_____
_____

8. A cowboy: _____
_____
_____
_____
_____

9. A Mormon: _____
_____
_____
_____

10. A youth like you: _____
_____
_____
_____

George Rogers Clark
(1752–1818)

Picture these American states: Ohio, Indiana, Illinois, Michigan, Wisconsin, and Minnesota. Now can you picture them belonging to Great Britain? George Clark is the person to thank for erasing that picture. He explored this region in the late eighteenth century. Back then it was called the Northwest Territory. And it was almost all wilderness. Great Britain owned it.

Clark was born in Charlottesville, Virginia. But he was destined to go west. He lived in Kentucky at the same time as Daniel Boone. Kentucky was wild and unsettled. Settlers had to defend their homes. Native Americans fought to keep settlers off their land. Then a new fight broke out. The American Revolution against Great Britain began.

Clark led an army of 200 Americans down the Ohio River. In winter the prairie was flooded with cold water and covered with ice. Clark and his men had to travel 160 miles in the rain. They sometimes waded in water up to their waists. More than once, they spent the night in wet, frozen clothes. The troops survived one of the most heroic marches on record.

The Americans captured three British forts. They even took Kaskaskia fort on July 4, 1778—American Independence Day. Britain lost the war. The vast Northwest Territory joined the United States.

Thomas Jefferson asked Clark to explore land west of the Mississippi River. He refused. But his younger brother William Clark said *yes*. William Clark joined Meriwether Lewis and made history of his own.

The Northwest Territory (Midwestern United States), 1778–1779

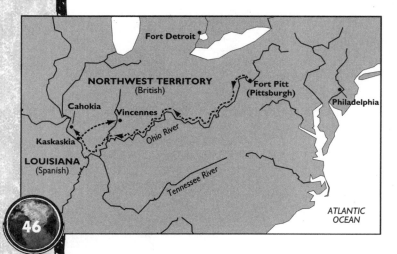

Mapmaker, Mapmaker

George Rogers Clark mapped the midwestern United States. Here are some ideas for places you might map: your bedroom, an ant farm, the way to school, the inside of your desk, the freckles on your arm, a garden. Choose one idea or think of your own. Draw your map below. You may need a ruler. You will need a pencil and an eraser.

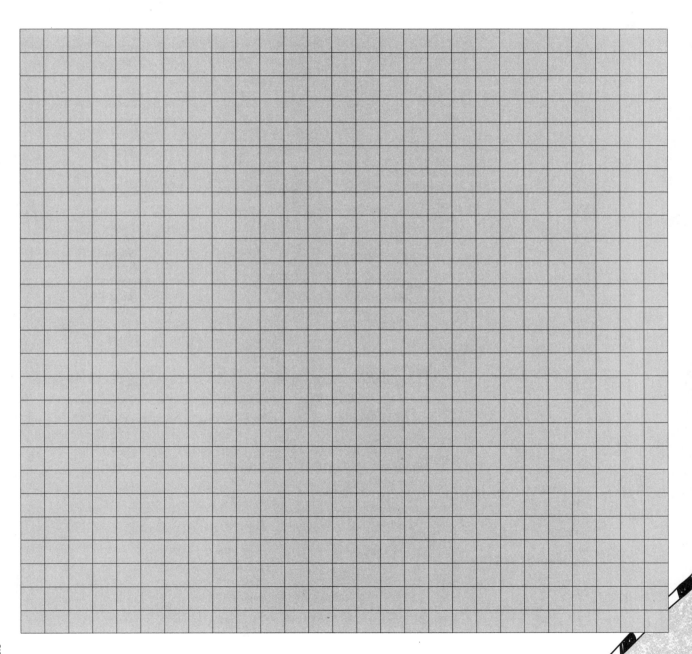

Where the Tribes Were

Native Americans, or Indians, lived all over the Americas.
How many of these tribes do you know? Choose one to study.
Report your findings to your class.

Eastern Woodlands
Abnaki
Malecite
Mahican
Mohegan
Iroquois
Huron
Potawatomi
Menominee
Sauk
Fox
Winnebago
Kickapoo
Illinois
Miami
Erie
Shawnee
Cherokee
Chickasaw
Natchez
Tunica
Yuchi
Choctaw
Chitimacha
Calusa
Seminole
Timucua
Yamasee
Creek
Catawba
Tuscarora
Powhatan
Delaware
Susquehanna
Narraganset
Wambanoag
Massachusetts

Far North
Chippewa
Ottawa
Algonquin
Montagnais
Micmac

Plains
Blackfeet
Assiniboine
Gros Ventre
Crow
Mandan
Arikara
Hidatsa
Sioux
Ponca
Omaha
Iowa
Cheyenne
Pawnee
Arapaho
Kiowa
Kansa
Osage
Quapaw
Wichita
Comanche
Caddo
Atakapa
Waco
Karankawa

California Inter-Mountain
Chinook Flathead
Klikitat
Klamath
Cayuse
Modoc
Karok
Hupa
Nez Percé
Bannock
Shoshoni
Wintun
Maidu
Paiute
Pomo
Chumash
Mohave
Luiseno
Gosuite
Ute
Diegueno

Southwest
Navaho
Hopi
Pueblo
Pima
Yuma
Papago
Maricopa
Apache
Yaqui
Cochimi
Waiguri

Middle American
Coahuiltec
Tamaulipec
Tarascan
Otomi
Toltec
Totonac
Aztec
Mixtec
Zapotec
Zoque
Olmec
Maya

Caribbean
Mosquito
Lenca
Guaymi
Cuna
Chocó
Barbacoa
Chibcha
Motilones
Tairona
Jirajara
Arawak
Goajiro
Carib
Taino
Subtaino
Ciboney
Lucayo

Andes
Cayapá
Colorado
Cañar
Mochica
Chimu
Chavín
Inca
Aymara
Uru

Tropical Forest
Taulipang
Omagua
Macu
Witoto
Yagua
Arawak
Jívaro
Tucuna
Yamamadí
Pano
Amahuaca
Campa

Northwest Coast
Nootka
Quileute
Quinalt
Salish
Kutenia
Yakima

NORTHWEST COAST
Nootka
Quileute
Quinalt
Salish
Kutenai
Yakima
Chinook Flathead
Klikitat
Cayuse

Blackfeet
Assiniboine
Gros Ventre
Crow
Mandan
Arikara
Hidatsa
Sioux
Cheyenne
Nez Percé
Bannock
Shoshoni

FAR NORTH
Chippewa
Menominee
Sauk
Winnebago
Ponca
Omaha
Iowa
Kickapoo
Miami
Illinois

Montagnais
Algonquin
Ottawa
Abnaki
Malecite
Micmac
Mahican
Mohegan
Huron
Iroquois
Massachusetts
Wambanoag

PLAINS
Pawnee
Kansa
Kiowa
Osage
Quapaw
Wichita
Comanche
Caddo
Waco
Atakapa
Apache

Klamath
Modoc
Karok
Hupa
Wintun
Pomo
Maidu
Paiute
Chumash
Mohave
Luiseno
Diegueno
Cochimi
Yaqui
Yuma
Papago
CALIFORNIA-INTERMOUNTAIN
Gosuite
Ute
Arapaho
Navaho
Hopi
Pima
Maricopa
Pueblo

EASTERN WOODLANDS
Shawnee
Cherokee
Chickasaw
Creek
Natchez
Yuchi
Tunica
Choctaw
Yamasee
Timucua
Chitimacha
Seminole
Calusa
Powhatan
Erie
Susquehanna
Delaware
Narraganset
Tuscarora
Catawba

ATLANTIC OCEAN

SOUTHWEST
Coahuiltec
Karankawa

MIDDLE AMERICAN
Tamaulipec
Waiguri
Tarascan
Otomi
Toltec
Aztec
Totonac
Mixtec
Zapotec
Olmec
Zoque
Maya

Gulf of Mexico

Ciboney
Subtaino
Lucayo
Taino
Carib

CARIBBEAN
Mosquito
Lenca
Guaymi
Cuna
Choco
Barbacoa
Goajiro
Tairona
Jirajara
Motilones
Chibcha
Arawak
Taulipang
Omagua
Macu
Arawak

PACIFIC OCEAN

ANDES
Cayapá
Colorado
Cañar
Jívaro
Witoto
Yagua
TROPICAL FOREST
Yamamadí
Tucuna
Mochica
Chimu
Chavín
Pano
Amahuaca
Campa
Inca
Aymara
Uru

Jean Baptiste Point du Sable
(1745?–1818)

A young slave named Suzanne worked on a Dutch plantation in the Caribbean. One day a French pirate and his band attacked. The pirate took everything he wanted—including Suzanne.

No longer a slave, Suzanne became a pirate's wife. In Haiti she gave birth to a boy. When the boy was 10, Suzanne died. The pirate became a merchant. The boy grew up rich and well-educated. His name was Jean Baptiste Point du Sable. Like his father, he too loved adventure.

Du Sable sailed to America, barely surviving a hurricane. He lived in the French city of New Orleans. Then the Spanish invaded. He moved to the French city of St. Louis. The British took over. Finally, du Sable went to Peoria, Illinois.

All this time, Europeans often mistook the Haitian for a runaway slave. Du Sable was safer among the Potawatomi Indians. He trapped and traded with them. Then he married one: Kittihawa.

Du Sable often went to Canada to trade. On the way, he had to pass a swamp called Eschikagou. So did other traders. In 1772, du Sable built a trading post there. Kittihawa and her people joined him. The pirate's son settled down. "Chicago" quickly became the area's busiest trading post.

There was one problem. Du Sable had dark skin, spoke French, and lived with Indians. The British thought he was a French spy. Twice they arrested du Sable but had to release him. After the arrests and the death of Kittihawa, the aging trader retired. He sold all his Chicago holdings. Then he lived—and died—in St. Charles, Missouri. The city of Chicago finally honored their founder in 1968.

Chicago, 1774

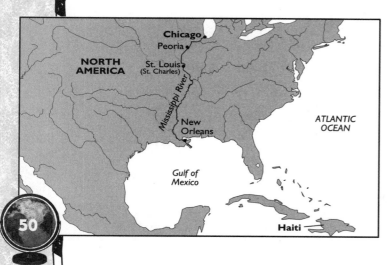

Stinking Onions

Eschikagou means "stinking onions." The name fit—until Jean Baptiste Point du Sable made it a city. Check out other names below. Do they fit?

Pick a place and research it. Or look up your own town name in a local library. Then write a letter to the mayor of the town. Explain why you think the name fits or doesn't fit. If it doesn't fit, suggest a new name. Be sure to explain why it's a better one.

- Amarillo, Texas: "yellow"
- Boise, Idaho: "wooded area"
- Fresno, California: "ash tree"
- Honolulu, Hawaii: "sheltered bay"
- Las Vegas, Nevada: "the plains"
- Los Angeles, California: "the angels"
- Milwaukee, Wisconsin: "good land and place of council"
- Minneapolis, Minnesota: "city of water falls"
- Mobile, Alabama: "movable"
- Pueblo, Colorado: "little village"
- Puerto Rico: "rich port"

_____

The place

Here are some facts I learned: _____

_____

_____

_____

_____

_____

_____

African Americans Build a Nation

Building a nation took people of all professions. These African Americans did their part and more.

WILLIAM A. LEIDESDORFF
Merchant

A simple sailor from the Virgin Islands, he died a millionaire at age 38. His trade ship ran between San Francisco and Hawaii.

XOXOXOXOXOXOXOXO

GEORGE MUNROE
Pony Express Rider

The Pony Express was a mail route on horseback. Neither snow, nor rain, nor gloom of night were the worst dangers. Riders such as George Munroe also feared bandits.

XOXOXOXOXOXOXOXO

"AUNT CLARA" BROWN
Pioneer

An early settler in Colorado, she opened the area's first laundry. "Aunt Clara" was free, but her family was enslaved. She used her profits to free more than 30 relatives.

XOXOXOXOXOXOXOXO

W. J. HARDIN
Politician

He was elected to state government in Wyoming. He helped start Wyoming's first adult education program.

BIDDY MASON
Businesswoman

As a slave, she cared for livestock. As an ex-slave, she set up businesses, including a day care center. She used her profits to buy land in Los Angeles.

XOXOXOXOXOXOXOXO

MARY FIELDS
Stagecoach Driver

She delivered mail and people in a stagecoach (a horse-drawn taxi). The job was rugged and dangerous, yet Fields worked until age 73.

XOXOXOXOXOXOXOXO

EDWARD ROSE
Interpreter

In the melting pot of America, people spoke hundreds of languages. Rose learned many Indian languages and interpreted for trappers and others.

XOXOXOXOXOXOXOXO

BOSE IKARD
Cowboy

He drove cattle for the famous Charles Goodnight. The Goodnight-Loving Trail ran from Texas to Montana.

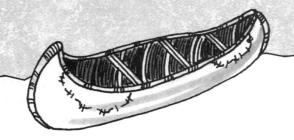

Part 4

They Blazed Western Trails

These explorers blazed trails clear to the Pacific Coast. The trails crossed Native American lands. They scaled the Rocky Mountains. Yet pioneers followed the trails. Permanent settlers followed the pioneers. America soon extended from coast to coast.

BIG QUESTIONS

- Why did explorers, pioneers, and settlers go into the wild West?
- Why did they attack Native Americans? Why did Native Americans attack them?
- Would you have risked a move to the West?

Sir Francis Drake
(1534?–1596)

**Pacific Coast,
1577–1580**

MAJOR ACHIEVEMENT:

He was the first Englishman to sail around the world. He explored the Pacific coast of North and South America.

Can one person be both a pirate and an admiral? A greedy profitseeker and a knight? Sir Francis Drake was all of the above.

As a British seaman, he saw traders kidnap Africans and sell them as slaves in America. African and Indian slaves worked in Spain's gold mines fueling its new empire.

Queen Elizabeth I of England took Spain's growing power as a threat. She had to weaken Spain without going to war. So she gave sea captains, money and ships. In return, they turned into terrifying pirates who raided Spanish ships for treasures. The queen, of course, took her share.

Of all the pirates, Drake was the most feared by Spain. In Peru, Spaniards had loaded pack animals with gold. Drake raided the whole convoy in a daring attack. He plundered towns and hijacked (took over) ships. Then he took all the Spanish gold back to England.

In 1577, Drake sailed for America with five pirate ships. Four sank. But on the last ship, Drake sailed around South America to the Pacific Coast. Between raids, he explored the area from Chile to Canada. Then Drake crossed the Pacific. When he reached England, his ship became the second one to circle the world. After this feat of exploration, Drake went back to pirating.

King Philip II of Spain grew angry. He wanted Drake punished. Instead, Queen Elizabeth made Drake a knight. King Philip was furious. In 1588 he unleashed his mighty fleet of warships, the Spanish Armada. The Spanish sailed up the English Channel. Drake, the new head of the navy, attacked from behind. He won. The battle changed history. England, not Spain, became the next world power.

A Pirate's Life

What do pirates look like? How do they live? What kinds of ships do they sail? Movies and books present many images of pirates. Use your imagination to create your idea of a pirate.

1. Pirate's Name: _____

2. Draw the ship's flag.

3. Draw your pirate's face.

4. Describe your pirate's lifestyle in a paragraph. _____

_____

_____

_____

_____

_____

_____

THE REAL THING

Use reference books to learn about a real pirate. The pirates named below lived from the sixteenth to the eighteenth centuries.

Jeanne Belville	Ali Pasha
Anne Bonny	"Calico Jack" Rackham
William Kidd	Mary Read
Edward Low	Edward Teach (Blackbeard)
Henry Morgan	Charles Vane

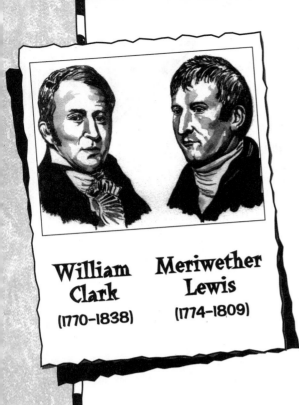

William Clark
(1770–1838)

Meriwether Lewis
(1774–1809)

The Oregon Country, 1804–1806

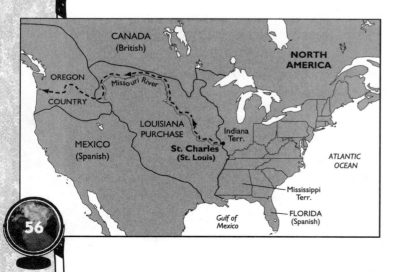

MAJOR ACHIEVEMENT:
They blazed a trail to the Pacific Ocean. The trail helped the United States claim the Oregon Territory.

President Thomas Jefferson himself ordered the expedition to the Pacific Ocean. He chose Meriwether Lewis, who chose William Clark. Their mission? Explore the Louisiana Territory—the large, wild land that America had just bought from France.

Lewis and Clark set out in 1804 from Missouri. But the real wilderness began in Mandan country (North Dakota). There were no maps or signs. At a fork in the Missouri River, Lewis and Clark had a fifty-fifty chance of choosing the right branch. They got lucky. But the next time they might not be lucky. Lewis and Clark convinced locals to guide them. The presence of Sacagawea, a Native American in the party, surely helped.

Getting lost was just one danger. Lewis shot a bison for food. He didn't reload the gun. A bear appeared and ran straight at him. There were no trees, no bushes, no rocks. So Lewis jumped in the river. The bear stopped at the water's edge. Then it just ran away.

In the Rocky Mountains the party received supplies from Sacagawea's people, the Shoshone. But crossing the mountains was slow. The party ran low on food again. This time, a Nez Percé tribe gave the travelers food and helped them make canoes.

In November the Pacific Ocean became visible. Clark wrote, "Great joy in Camp. We are in view of the ocean which we have been so long to see...."

"The expedition became famous. Lewis and Clark made friends with many Native Americans. They mapped and studied unexplored land. And Jefferson took more interest in the Oregon Country. He wanted to make it part of the United States.

Go West!

Lewis and Clark set out to follow the Missouri River to its source in the hopes of finding an all-water route to the Pacific Ocean. They sailed up the Missouri River and rode over the Rocky Mountains until they finally reached the Pacific coast. The expedition covered 7,500 miles and took two years and four months!

After Lewis and Clark had opened a trail, settlers traveled west to settle new lands. How did these people travel in the early 1800s? Below are the two chief means of transportation.

Prairie Schooners

Many families traveled west in heavy wagons called *Conestoga wagons*. These wagons had large white canvas tops. The wagons looked like sailboats and were nicknamed *prairie schooners* (a schooner is a kind of sailing ship).

Stagecoaches

The only form of *public* transportation in the early 1800s was the passenger coach. The coach driver had to change horses at *stages* along the way (about every 15 miles), which is why the horse-drawn coaches came to be called *stagecoaches*.

MOVING ON UP (or under)—and Away!

Some say the next frontiers will be underwater and in space. Imagine a colony of new settlers either in space or under the sea. Invent a means of transportation that would be an efficient way for people to travel, to commute to and from work, and so on. (A sub-subway, anyone?) On the back of this page, draw your mode of transportation and describe how it works.

Sacagawea
(1787?–1812?)

Imagine being a ten-year-old Shoshone girl. Warriors attack your Rocky Mountain home. They take you hundreds of miles away. You work as a slave for five long years. Will you ever see your family again?

That was Sacagawea's unlucky start in life. Then along came a trader named Toussaint Charbonneau. He married Sacagawea's friend Otter Woman. Then he married Sacagawea. The family joined the Lewis and Clark expedition. Halfway into it, Sacagawea had her first baby, a son. She carried little Pomp the rest of the way.

The explorers ran low on supplies. To win food from Indians, an African American named York performed feats of strength. Sacagawea found plants to eat. Then, an explorer wrote, "Sacagawea began to dance and show extraordinary joy . . . pointing to several Indians, sucking her fingers to show they were of her tribe." Sacagawea was home! The explorer added, "As we approached, a woman made her way through the crowd toward Sacagawea. They embraced with tender affection. They had been childhood friends." Like Sacagawea, the woman had been stolen by warriors but escaped.

Pacific Northwest, 1804–1806

The explorers met Chief Cameahwait. Sacagawea was interpreting, when she suddenly jumped up. The chief was her brother! Sadly, only two brothers and a nephew remained of her family. The chief offered food, guides, and horses. Even with these supplies, the group half-starved. Without them, some may have died.

Sacagawea earned Missouri land for her part in the expedition. But in time, she moved to her homeland. Some say she lived to age 95. But she probably died around age 25.

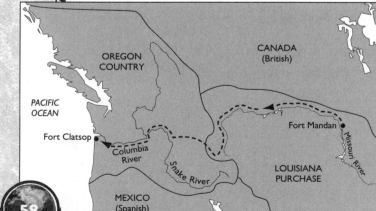

Plants to Use and Amuse

Sacagawea knew how to use plants for food, medicine, clothing, and dyes.
Read about seven plants and their uses below. Then do some research.
Add one fact for each plant.*

1. **Torch Flower** *(Mullein)* People dipped the stem in grease. Then they
   lit the grease to make a torch. _____

   _____

2. **Buttercup** Children folded and squeezed the yellow petals to make a
   pop sound. _____

   _____

3. **Honeysuckle** People pulled apart the trumpet-shaped flowers. Then
   they drank the "honey" (nectar) in the base of the flower. _____

   _____

4. **Cattail** The Ojibwas wove the leaves into mats and ate the inner part
   of the stalks. _____

   _____

5. **Trillium** People ground the plant and mixed it with lard. The lotion
   helped soothe bee stings. _____

   _____

6. **Aloe** This spikey desert plant provided medicine, fiber,
   and hand lotion. _____

   _____

7. **Dandelion** Apaches ate dandelions the way we eat vegetables. _____

   _____

*Here is a good reference to look for: Shanberg, Karen and Stan Tekiela. *Plantworks*.
(Cambridge, MN: Adventure Publications, 1991).

George Washington Bush
(1791?–1863)

MAJOR ACHIEVEMENT:
He led the first colony of Americans
to the shores of Puget Sound, Washington.

In 1814 the United States and Great Britain warred over New Orleans. A Missouri native, George Washington Bush, fought for the United States. His commander was Major General Andrew Jackson. Jackson later became President of the United States. Bush joined the Hudson's Bay Company, the first and most famous fur trading company. He traveled to the Pacific coast to buy furs. Bush quickly vowed to settle there.

In 1843 Bush led his family and seven white families out west. The wagon train took the Oregon Trail to the Columbia River valley in Oregon. Many settlers set down roots there. But Bush wanted to live in a free territory. He hoped to avoid slavery and racism at all costs.

The wagon train rolled into Puget Sound, Washington. Bush and the others were the first Americans to settle there. The settlement was called Tumwater. Bush built a mill for lumber and wheat. It was powered by an eight-foot waterfall. The settlers planted crops on the untouched land.

Meanwhile, Great Britain and the United States argued over Washington territory. Americans used the Tumwater settlement to boost their case, since citizens already lived there. The United States gained the land south of today's United States-Canadian border.

Meanwhile, Bush became a wealthy farmer. One of his sons raised a prized wheat crop. A sample is on display at the Smithsonian Institution in Washington, D.C. After Bush died, his son William Owens joined the Washington state legislature.

The Oregon Country, 1820s

Willamette Valley

Puget Sound

LOUISIANA PURCHASE

OREGON COUNTRY

PACIFIC OCEAN

Oregon Trail

MEXICO (Spanish)

Colorado River

You Name It

The first explorers to reach an area got to name everything. Mountain peaks, rivers, valleys, towns—they named them. Can you find these strange names on a map of the United States? Use the map's index to help you.

- Total Wreck, Arizona
- Hope, Arkansas
- Rough and Ready, California
- Happy, Kentucky
- Truth or Consequences, New Mexico
- Pongokwayhaymock Lake, Maine
- Bad Axe, Michigan

- Cheesequake, New Jersey
- Welcome, North Carolina
- Delightful, Ohio
- Yum Yum, Tennessee
- Comfort, Texas
- Friendly, West Virginia
- Maneater Canyon, Wyoming

YOUR TOWN

List ten names of streets, streams, parks, and so on, in your community.

_____

_____

_____

Do the names have anything in common? _____

_____

Can you guess their origin? _____

_____

Which names would you change, and why? _____

_____

_____

_____

John Charles Frémont
(1813–1890)

Kit Carson
(1809–1868)

John Charles Frémont explored for the United States government. He had two basic orders. First, claim western territory for the United States. Second, make friends with Californians. Mexico ruled California, and the United States government wanted it.

Frémont made five expeditions in the area between the Rocky Mountains and the Pacific Ocean. On the first one, he met frontiersman Kit Carson. They became lifelong friends. Carson knew how to live in the wilderness. He had been a trapper in Arizona, California, Idaho, and the Rocky Mountains.

Carson guided Frémont's men down the Oregon Trail. The trail took settlers to the Oregon Country. The Sioux Indians grew hostile as more and more people crossed their land. Thanks to Carson, the explorers made it safely through. At South Pass, Wyoming, Frémont planted an American flag on Frémont Peak.

Carson guided many of Frémont's expeditions. They explored the Great Salt Lake in Utah, the area from Colorado to California, and Oregon. On an expedition to the Southwest, Frémont helped make the first scientific map of the West. The map aided many future travelers. It also made both Frémont and Carson famous.

Frémont later ran for president of the United States. He came from Georgia, in the South. Yet he opposed slavery. Frémont lost to James Buchanan because of this. In the American Civil War, Frémont joined the Union army (in the North). He later served as a governor of Arizona.

Rocky Mountains and Oregon Country, 1842–1844

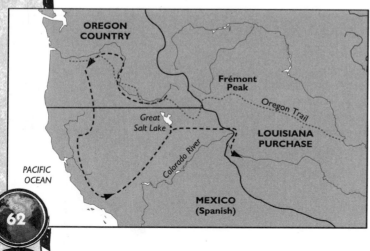

Okay Bayou?

Kit Carson and many other explorers learned Native American words wherever they went. Many words we use today came from native languages.

Which ones below do you know? Choose five words and use them in a short story.

Bayou (from *bayuk*): an outlet of a lake or river

Cashew (from *acajú*): a type of nut

Chocolate: a food made from cacao

Igloo (from *iglu*): a domed home

Kayak: a watertight canoe

Maize: corn

Moccasin (from *mockasin*): a flat leather shoe or slipper

Parka: a heavy jacket with a hood

Piranha: a type of predator fish

Potato (from *batata*): a tuber, or root, that's edible

Savanna (from *zabana*): a plain

_____

_____

_____

_____

_____

_____

_____

_____

_____

_____

_____

_____

_____

_____

_____

Wagons West

By the mid-1800s, explorers made an American dream come true. They helped the nation stretch from coast to coast. They had scouted mountain passes, river crossings, water holes, and more.

Now pioneers could ride these fresh trails. Their wagons went only a mile or two per hour. The journey took months. But, finally, settlers could reach the west coast. The Santa Fe, Oregon, and California trails were the best ways to get there. Which one would you take? On the next page, explain your answer.

SANTA FE TRAIL

In 1821 traders in Kansas City, Missouri, rode goods to Santa Fe, New Mexico. The Santa Fe Trail was born. Drivers had to circle the wagons to keep out raiders. But the trail itself was easy. The tougher Old Spanish Trail continued from Santa Fe to Los Angeles, California. Only pack mules could make it.

OREGON TRAIL

In 1843 a thousand pioneers and their cattle made tracks along the Platte River. On this Oregon Trail, many died of a disease called cholera or from thirst and starvation. Near the end, survivors faced the Columbia River. They floated their wagons down the river to a fort. Livestock crossed over the mountains.

CALIFORNIA TRAIL

In 1844 the first wagons crossed the Sierra Nevada mountains into California. The California Trail followed the Oregon Trail to Utah. There, many pioneers took shortcuts over the mountains. And many died. Of the famous Donner party, only about half survived. The trail ended in San Francisco.

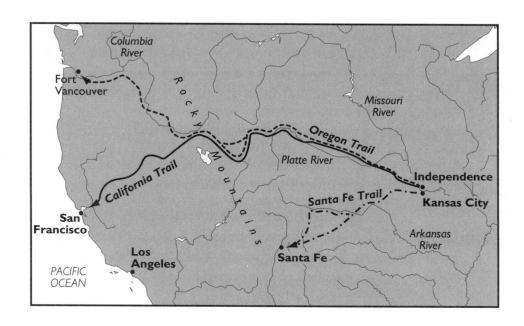

_____
_____
_____
_____
_____
_____
_____
_____
_____
_____
_____
_____
_____
_____

James Beckwourth
(1798–1867)

Settlements marked the American frontier. Mountain men lived beyond this frontier. These rugged men tamed the wilderness for future settlers. James Beckwourth was one of the most skilled mountain men in the west.

Like other mountain men, Beckwourth had a strong independent streak. He left his family in Virginia. His mother was a slave. His father was an officer. Beckwourth sailed to the unexplored Louisiana Territory. But people treated him badly.

Farther west, skin color did not matter much. Strength and bravery counted. So Beckwourth joined an expedition to the Rocky Mountains. A fur company paid the way. Beckwourth trapped many hard-to-catch animals. He helped to blaze new trails and map the wilderness. He earned the respect of everyone.

The fur company sent Beckwourth on another expedition. He was to meet a trapper named Bill Sublette in the Great Salt Lake region of Utah. Sublette proposed that they set up a trading post among the Blackfoot Indians. The job was dangerous. But Beckwourth gave it a try. His dark skin helped him blend with the Blackfeet. He even married a Blackfoot and settled for a while.

Beckwourth became a warrior and chief among the Crow Indians nicknamed Morning Star. After many years he went to Missouri to settle down. When the gold rush started, Beckwourth headed west. In 1850, he discovered what today is called Beckwourth Pass. On a peace mission with the Crows, Beckwourth died of food poisoning. The Crows buried him among chiefs. Beckwourth Pass, Beckwourth, and Beckwourth Peak are named in his honor.

Rocky Mountains and Great Salt Lake Region, 1828 and 1850

Columbia River
Snake River
Missouri River
Rocky Mountains
Oregon Trail
Platte River
Beckwourth Pass
California Trail
Salt Lake City
PACIFIC OCEAN
Sierra Nevada
San Francisco
Santa Fe Trail
Los Angeles
Santa Fe

Tell It on the Mountain

Mountain men like James Beckwourth still meet once each year. The meeting is called a *rendezvous*. Everyone tells a tall tale about a scary or funny experience. In a tall tale, it's okay to exaggerate (make bigger) the facts. The idea is to make the story interesting.

Here's how it works.

- Take a real event: James Beckwourth walked a wild grizzly bear down Main Street.

- Exaggerate the facts. How big was the bear? How scared were the townspeople? What did the bear do? What did Beckwourth do?

Write your tall tale here. _____

_____

_____

_____

_____

_____

_____

_____

_____

_____

_____

_____

_____

_____

_____

_____

_____

Isabella Bird Bishop
(1831–1904)

MAJOR ACHIEVEMENT:
Her books described little-traveled parts of the globe. She inspired other women to explore.

An explorer has to cross seas, deserts, and mountains. Such a person must be strong and tough. So how did Isabella Bird Bishop ever make it as an explorer? She spent her childhood sickly and frail. At age 18 she had a nasty tumor in her back. She could hardly walk, let alone trot around the globe!

Bishop's doctor thought traveling would revive her. Nothing else had worked. So at age 23, she sailed to Canada. Amazing! She was bursting with energy! Bishop toured Montreal, Toronto, Chicago, and New England. She even wrote a book: *The Englishwoman in America.*

Back home, Bishop fell ill again. Her doctor prescribed another trip. Bishop took it further. She made traveling her career: "It's like living in a new world, so free, so fresh, so vital, so careless, so full of interest that one grudges being asleep."

From Australia, Bishop sailed to the Sandwich Islands (now Hawaii). A 12-hour hurricane scared most of the people. But Bishop was thrilled. The storm charged her with even more energy. In Hawaii she climbed live volcanoes and rode horses as men did. (Other women rode sidesaddle.) In Colorado she saw mining camps and ranches, drove wagons, and herded cattle. The once sickly child explored 15,000-foot mountains on horseback!

Bishop's voyages grew more daring. Her many books were widely read. The Royal Geographical Society in Britain made her one of the first female members. A reporter wrote, "She laughed at fatigue, she was indifferent to danger."

Where in the World Is Isabella Bird?

Isabella Bird Bishop journeyed to every continent except Antarctica. Read the events from her travels. Then match the events with the countries where they happened. If you get stuck, look up the words in bold for clues.

_____ **1.** After leaving the capital city of **Auckland**, her ship hit a hurricane.

_____ **2.** In **northern Africa**, her horse was so tall that she mounted it with a ladder.

_____ **3.** She floated 2,000 miles on the **Yangtze River** to the city of **Shanghai**.

_____ **4.** She camped on **The Big Island** near a fiery volcano named **Moana Loa**.

_____ **5.** She road a **yak** on some of the **highest mountains in the world**.

_____ **6.** In the **Rocky Mountains**, she met the famous Comanche Bill.

_____ **7.** On a **tropical peninsula in Southeast Asia**, she dined at a table with apes.

_____ **8.** She rode 1,000 miles in **Kurdistan**, now in the countries of **Iraq and Iran**.

Countries

A. China

B. Malaya (now Malaysia)

C. Morocco

D. New Zealand

E. Persia

F. Sandwich Islands (now Hawaii)

G. Tibet

H. United States

Women in the Wilderness

Before the nineteenth century, few women explored. No one would sponsor them. Instead, sponsors gave ships, a crew, and supplies to male explorers. In the mid-1800s, a few women struck out anyway. Some were rich, so they paid their own way. Others had jobs that took them into the wilderness. Today, women have explored the Poles, the ocean, space—everywhere.

Margery Kempe
Pilgrim

In the early 1400s, she journeyed across Europe to Jerusalem, in the Middle East. She was the first woman to write a travel book.

Jeanne Baret
Adventuress

Dressed as a man, she sailed around the world from 1767 to 1769. The expedition leader was famous explorer Louis-Antoine de Bougainville.

May French Sheldon
Traveler

She explored Masai country in East Africa. In the nineteenth century the region was very hard to reach.

Amelia Earhart
Pilot

She was the first woman to fly across the Atlantic Ocean. Crossing the Pacific, she and her plane vanished.

Margaret Bourke-White
Photographer

She traveled to India, Africa, the Far East, and Russia to take award-winning photographs.

Maria Sibylla Merian
Painter of Nature

In the seventeenth century, she painted new plants and animals in Surinam (now Suriname), South America.

Kate Field
Journalist

Female reporters were rare in the nineteenth century. But Field managed to travel well off the beaten track in her job.

Annie Peck Smith
Professor

In 1908 she was the first to scale the highest mountain in Peru, South America. She climbed until she was 82.

Elsie C. Parsons & Ruth Benedict
Anthropologists

They studied Native American cultures in the Southwest, California, Montana, Mexico, Peru, and the Caribbean.

Eugenie Clark
Scientist

She is famous for her work with sharks. On one of many underwater adventures, Clark found 7,000-year-old human remains.

Behind Closed Doors

Margaret Bourke-White said, "Nothing attracts me like a closed door." What do you think she meant? What were the "closed doors" that she had to open? Write a paragraph to explain the quotation. Use the back of this page.

Part 5

They Aim for New Frontiers

Is there anyplace left to explore? Where are today's frontiers? Modern explorers find them in the extreme. They dive to ocean bottoms. They go to the top of the world. And they leave our world altogether. Space is the newest and toughest frontier.

BIG QUESTIONS

- Why do today's explorers explore?
- Have the reasons for exploring changed over the years?
- Would you rather be a modern-day explorer or one from the past?

71

Matthew Henson
(1866–1955)

Robert E. Peary
(1856–1920)

By the late 1800s, America was pretty much tamed. So explorers looked elsewhere for thrills. "Arctic fever" swept the land. The race was on to reach the North Pole. A Navy officer named Robert E. Peary devoted his life to it. Matthew Henson joined him every step of the way. After having sailed the world as a cabin boy, Henson had a strong taste for adventure.

The first attempts were by sea. After all, the North Pole was in the Arctic Ocean. Peary and Henson's ship came the closest of any ship. But the polar pack ice (chunks of ice) swirled too fast. Ships couldn't cross it or break through the solid ice.

The explorers took a new approach: dog sleds. They borrowed their sled design from Etah Inuits (Eskimos). Peary and Henson spent dark arctic winters with the Etahs. The Etahs admired Henson, or "Matthew the Kind One." They showed their guests how to survive in sub-zero temperatures. Many Etahs carried food and supplies on the polar journeys.

Peary and Henson made their attempts in spring. Several failed. Then in 1909 they set out again. They had 50 days to reach the Pole and return. Any longer, and both dogs and men would give out.

Several times, Peary sent people back. In the end, only six remained: Peary, Henson, and four Etahs—Ootah, Egingwah, Seegloo, and Ooqueah. They forced themselves to travel 20 hours per day. On April 6, both Peary and Henson thought they were close. Peary read their position on his sextant. The party had overshot the Pole by seven miles! They backtracked and took new readings. Finally, Peary and Henson were on top of the world!

The North Pole, 1909

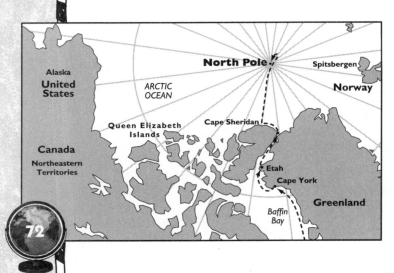

Number One

Matthew Henson and Robert Peary were the first to stand on the North Pole. The first to fly over it was Richard Byrd in 1926. The first to cruise over it in a submarine was the crew of the *Nautilus* in 1959. Being first is a burning goal of many explorers.

Have you ever been first? Has someone in your life?

Write a news story about a first feat.

Remember to tell:
- **who** did it
- **what** was done
- **where** it happened
- **when** it happened
- **why** or **how** the person did it

TODAY'S NEWS

Louise Arner Boyd
(1887–1972)

When Louise Arner Boyd was a child, the race for the North Pole had just begun. She was 22 years old when Robert Peary and Matthew Henson finally reached their goal. Boyd's interest in the Arctic was just beginning.

In 1924, Boyd vacationed on Spitsbergen. The icy land was harsh and cold. But not to Boyd: "Far north, hidden behind grim barriers of pack ice, are lands that hold one spellbound."

Polar regions were costly to reach. But Boyd was rich. She ran a business, lived in a mansion, and had a maid. In the end, Boyd traded it all in for the chance to explore. She spent most of her money on expeditions—a crew, a ship, and supplies.

Boyd sailed the eastern coast of Greenland, land of icebergs and glaciers. She explored the Franz Joseph Fjord extensively. On every trip, Boyd took her maid, fine clothes, and makeup. But she roughed it when necessary. The scientists studied rocks, plants, and landforms. Boyd photographed many unexplored lands. In World War II (1939–1945) she rescued her photos in Norway just before Germany invaded. The photos helped American ships navigate Arctic waters.

In 1933, Boyd's ship ran aground. A dark winter trapped in ice could be horrifying. So the crew threw supplies on shore to lighten the ship. Then they lassoed (roped) an iceberg. The iceberg towed the ship off the bank.

On her last expedition in 1941, Boyd sailed just 800 miles from the North Pole. She set a record by landing on the northernmost point in Greenland. In 1955, at the age of 67, she became the first woman to fly over the North Pole.

The Arctic, 1931–1938

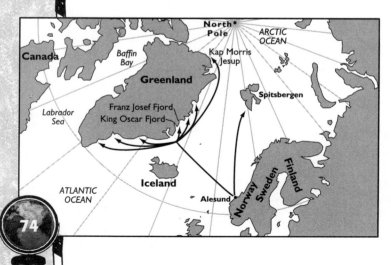

A Fortune to Freeze

Louise Arner Boyd spent a fortune to **explore** the frozen Arctic. Why did she do it? Read some of her reasons, **below**. Add your own reasons. Then pretend you are an explorer in the Arctic. Write a letter to someone you love. In it, explain why you are risking your **life** and life's fortune.

Boyd's Reasons	**Other Reasons**
It's thrilling.	_____
I see places before anyone else on earth does.	_____
Geographers can map new lands, thanks to my photos.	_____
Scientists can study new plants, animals, and rocks.	_____
I meet Inuits (Eskimos).	_____

Dear

Polar Explorers
What Were They Thinking?

It's the middle of nowhere. The temperature is 50 degrees below zero. Storm winds blow 100 miles per hour. What would you be thinking? Here's what some of the greatest polar explorers had on their minds.

"Every day we have been ready to start for our depot 11 miles away. But outside the door . . . remains a scene of whirling drift. I do not think we can hope for better things now. We shall stick it out to the end. But we are getting weaker, of course, and the end cannot be far."

(Robert Scott, who reached the South Pole only to find Raold Amundson's flag. On the way back, Scott and two men got stuck in a storm and died just 11 miles from food and fuel.)

"Pride and affection shone in the five pairs of eyes that gazed upon the flag. I had determined that planting it should be equally divided. It was not for one man to do this; it was for all who had staked their lives. . . . Five weather-beaten, frost-bitten fists grasped the pole, raised the waving flag, and planted it as the first at the South Pole."

(Raold Amundson, the first to reach the South Pole (1911). He was 35 days ahead of Robert Scott.)

"Our spirit can carry us through seemingly impossible tasks. I have been in survival situations, out of food in subzero weather, where my spirit carried me through. To an observer, my survival may have looked impossible. But spirit, our driving power, cannot easily be explained; it can only be felt."

(Will Steger, who has driven dog sleds to both Poles and beyond. In 1989–1990, he and a team of adventurers crossed Antarctica: 3,700 miles in seven months.)

Ann went out front to coax the dogs over a gap. Then she dropped out of sight. The snow gave way and she plunged into the ocean. She flung her arms wide to bridge the gap and wriggled up the the edge. It was 30 degrees below zero. But Ann said, "It was a good day for a dunk because there was no wind." She simply dressed in dry clothes and got on her way in minutes.

(Ann Bancroft, the only woman on a 1,000-mile journey to the North Pole in 1986. Will Steger, the leader, described the accident in his book North to the Pole.*)*

"All these men had a blind confidence that I would somehow get them back to land. All the [thrust] centered in me. Whatever pace I set, the others would make good. But if I played out, they would stop like a car with a punctured tire."

(Robert Peary, first to reach the North Pole along with Matthew Henson.)

Robert Ballard
(1942–)

Robert Ballard says, "I've spent my whole life dreaming up things and then going out and doing them." His first big dream came from the novel, *20,000 Leagues Under the Sea* by Jules Verne. In it, Captain Nemo powers a submarine into murky, unknown waters.

First, Ballard had to learn about the ocean. He studied geology, chemistry, ocean science, and technology. Then he used all that knowledge to build *Alvin*. *Alvin* is a mini-submarine for exploring the ocean floor.

Ballard didn't expect to find sea monsters, as Captain Nemo did. But he came close. In 1979 the *Alvin* crew discovered deep-sea vents. From *Alvin*, Ballard saw hot chemicals shoot out of them. All around were strange clams, giant tube worms, and other *weird* creatures.

Many scientists, especially Ballard, used Alvin to study rocks and marine life. The sub was cold and cramped. It took hours to hit bottom. If people got stuck there, they could die.

In the 1980s, Ballard built a robot team called *Argo* and *Jason*. Humans control them from a ship. The team's first mission was to find the *Titanic*—the famous ship that sank in 1912. Treasure hunters had looked long and hard for it.

In 1985, French scientists used sonar (sound waves). Where they got a strange blip, Ballard unleashed *Argo* and *Jason*. The pair of robots soon found the *Titanic* about 13,000 feet down!

Argo and *Jason* have since explored many shipwrecks. Each year, Ballard hosts a live show. The robots search the ocean. Humans follow along on a video screen. Some even drive the robots. In a way, Ballard has made explorers of us all.

Jason Robot Submarine

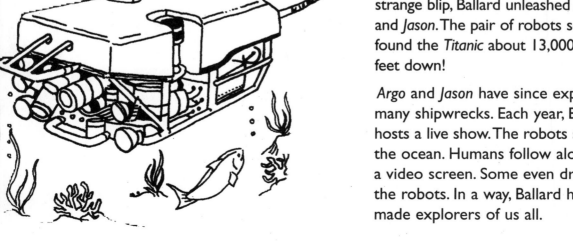

Captain's Log

Jason and Argo are robot explorers. They searched these shipwreck sites. Choose one and research the facts. (For *Isis*, look up Roman trading vessels in general.) Then write a ship's log entries for the days before the disaster.

Titanic

British luxury liner. Thought to be unsinkable. Hit an iceberg and sank in 1912.

Lusitania

British ship. Hit by a German torpedo off the Irish coast. Sank in 1915 during World War I.

Isis
(real name unknown)

Ancient Roman ship. Carried amphoras (vases) of goods. Sank in the Mediterranean Sea.

Bismarck

German battleship. Cornered off the French coast. Sank in 1941—early in World War II.

Time	Log	Course	Speed	Weather	Remarks

Sylvia Alice Earle
(1935–)

MAJOR ACHIEVEMENT:

Earle has been exploring ocean depths around the world since the 1950s. She made the deepest solo dive without a cable. She pioneered the use of deep-sea submersibles (minisubmarines).

It all began when the Earle family moved. In New Jersey, young Sylvia had had a pond in the backyard. In the new Florida home, her backyard was the Gulf of Mexico. For a girl who loved to be anywhere near water, this was paradise.

Earle began scuba diving as a teenager. She graduated early from both high school and college. Her degree was in marine botany (sea plants). Then the adventure began.

In 1970, Earle signed on for an experiment called Tektite II. NASA wanted to know how future astronauts would cope with being cut off from people. With four other scientists, Earle lived 50 feet underwater. For weeks, their home was two watertight tanks and a walkway.

In 1979, Earle donned a deep-sea diving suit. She sank into the sea. It grew dark except for glowing sea creatures. When Earle hit bottom, she had set a record for depth: 1,250 feet. As she planted a United States flag, water pressed on her suit with a force of 600 pounds per square inch. Divers said it was the most daring dive ever made. One claimed Earle had "nerves of steel."

Earle wanted to go deeper. She and a partner built submersibles—car-sized submarines. One called *Deep Rover* took her 3,000 feet down. Earle's goal is 35,800 feet—the very deepest parts of the ocean. That's deeper than Mount Everest is high.

To Sylvia Earle, the ocean is the biggest aquarium on Earth. The best part is, there are still vast forests, mountains, deserts, and canyons to explore within it.

Risky or Reckless?

Sylvia Earle is an expert diver. So going for a depth record was risky, but not too risky. For a beginning diver the same feat would be reckless. The risk of dying would be more than the chance of surviving.

Would these feats be risky or reckless for you? Circle your answers, then explain each in a complete sentence.

1. Jumping a curb on a skateboard.   *Risky*   *Reckless*

_____

_____

2. Walking on your hands to win a bet.   *Risky*   *Reckless*

_____

_____

3. Taking a bus to a strange part of town.   *Risky*   *Reckless*

_____

_____

4. Camping in a park with grizzly bears.   *Risky*   *Reckless*

_____

_____

5. Eating meat that has a funny odor.   *Risky*   *Reckless*

_____

_____

6. Going out in winter with no mittens.   *Risky*   *Reckless*

_____

_____

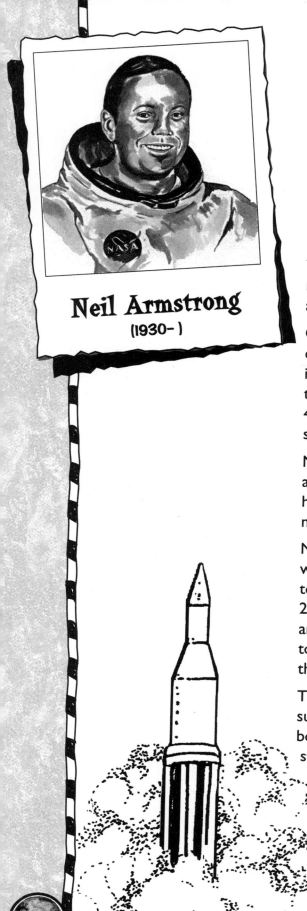

Neil Armstrong
(1930–)

The future always looked up for Neil Armstrong. He rode in an airplane at age 6. He made airplane models at age 9. He flew airplanes by age 16.

One of his teachers said, "He wanted to do something daring and different." Something daring was to be a pilot in the Korean War (1950–1953). Armstrong flew 200 test planes and helicopters. One rocket plane zoomed 4,000 miles per hour and soared 40 miles high! And something different? To walk on the moon.

NASA, the space agency, chose Armstrong for the astronaut corps in 1962. After years of intense training, he got a flight. Armstrong flew the two-man Gemini 8 mission. It was just a warm-up.

NASA graduated to three-person Apollo ships. Apollo 8 was the first to *circle* the moon. Armstrong was assigned to Apollo 11 with Buzz Aldrin and Mike Collins. On July 20, 1969, Collins orbited the moon in the capsule. Aldrin and Armstrong dropped gently in the moon lander. Then touchdown! They were the first humans to land on the moon!

The moon crew spent six hours putting on special space suits. Then Armstrong took the first awkward step. He bounced in the weaker gravity. He said, "That's one small step for man, one giant leap for mankind." For two days the astronauts gathered moon rocks and took pictures.

All three astronauts were heroes. Major cities had parades. The trio visited 22 countries. The fanfare faded in time, but Armstrong's foot prints on the moon won't. Barring meteors, they'll stay fresh for millions of years!

Who Owns the Moon?

Like other explorers, Neil Armstrong planted an American flag. Does that mean the United States owns the moon? What if another country planted a flag? Would it own the moon? Perhaps every country should own part of the moon. What do you think? Write a Moon Treaty that spells out who—if anyone—owns the moon.

_____

_____

_____

_____

_____

_____

_____

_____

_____

_____

_____

_____

_____

_____

_____

_____

_____

_____

_____

_____

_____

Sally Kristen Ride
(1951–)

MAJOR ACHIEVEMENT:
She was the first American woman in space. She handled satellites, robot arms, and science experiments.

In the early 1960s the first Americans blasted into space. They were all men. NASA, the space agency, banned women. Many girls grew up thinking that becoming an astronaut was impossible. Sally Ride was one of them.

In the 1970s, NASA lifted the ban. The agency needed top-flight scientists. Eight thousand people applied in 1978. About 1,000 were women. One was Sally Ride.

Her background was ideal. As a girl in California, she was an outstanding tennis player. Billie Jean King and Alice Marble, two great players of the past, encouraged Ride to turn pro. She went back to college instead. Ride loved Shakespeare, the great English writer. But she loved science more. She earned a doctorate (the top degree) in astrophysics (astronomy plus physics).

Ride and a few other scientists made it into the astronaut corps. She trained hard, even learning to fly a jet. Captain Robert L. Crippen picked her for a mission. It's because she's a woman, some people said. Crippen was annoyed.

"She is flying with us because she is the very best person for the job," he said. "There is no man I would rather have in her place."

Space Shuttle Missions, 1983, 1984

On June 18, 1983, Sally Ride became the first American woman in space. (Soviet Valentina Tereshkova was the first woman.) Ride sent two satellites on their way. She tested the new robot arm. She did 40 science experiments. "It was the most fun I ever had in my life," she said.

Ride flew again in 1984. Another woman, Kathryn Sullivan, was in the crew. Millions of girls watched them soar into space. Some of those girls are now in the space program. They knew it was possible all along.

Career Ladder

Key choices can put your life on a new course. Dr. Sally Ride almost became a professional tennis player, a Shakespeare expert, and a science researcher. But she applied to NASA, and she ended up as an astronaut.

Think of a career you might someday like to have. How do you imagine getting there? Fill in the steps for planning and realizing your career goals.

Suppose you make a different choice at one of the steps. How might your career change? Draw and fill in a new ladder on the back of this page.

Challenger's Last Voyage
January 1986

Explorers face danger with calm and intelligence. They have broad knowledge and sharp skills—dog sledding, sailing, diving. They plan ahead. They lead and inspire others. But sometimes, they're just plain unlucky. Weather systems kick up at the worst times. Disease or injury strike. Accidents happen.

One tragic accident occurred in January 1986. Seven astronauts lifted off in the Challenger space shuttle. Like other explorers, they were highly skilled. They stayed calm under pressure. But in the end, none of that mattered. After 73 seconds, 50,800 feet above Earth, the shuttle exploded. The seven astronauts were helpless to stop it. Students across the country had watched the liftoff on TV. They were waiting to see the teacher-astronaut in space. Families and friends of all the astronauts were in shock. The nation mourned.

The seven Challenger astronauts had given their lives in the spirit of exploration. For that, they became America's heroes. Their courage has inspired a new generation of explorers—on Earth and above it.

The crew of *Challenger* 51-L *(left to right):* front row: Michael J. Smith, pilot; Francis R. (Dick) Scobee, commander; Ronald E. McNair, Mission Specialist 3. Rear row: Ellison S. Onizuka, Mission Specialist 1; S. Christa McAuliffe, Payload Specialist 1; Gregory B. Jarvis, Payload Specialist 2; Judith A. Resnik, Mission Specialist 2. (NASA)

Lucky 13

On the Apollo 13 mission in 1970, a tank exploded. The crew was losing oxygen, heat, and power. Where could they get more? Only planet Earth. No other known place in the universe has what we need to survive.

Luckily, the Apollo crew made it home. Other explorers in history didn't. They ran out of supplies and couldn't replace them. For each location listed below, choose the essential items explorers must take with them (things that can't be found in case of emergency).

- **Fresh Water**   • **Food**   • **Air**
- **Shelter (from harsh weather)**   • **Transportation (to get home)**

Locations

Space _____

_____

The Open Ocean _____

_____

Tropical Islands _____

_____

The Desert _____

_____

The Arctic _____

_____

The Woods _____

_____

In your opinion, which locations are most dangerous? _____

_____

_____

Least dangerous? _____

_____

_____

Franklin Chang-Diaz
(1950–)

MAJOR ACHIEVEMENT:

A space veteran, Chang-Diaz is designing a rocket system for future human missions to Mars.

In four missions, Franklin Chang-Diaz has spent 656 hours in space. So he's had plenty of time to check out the sights.

"Earth's atmosphere looks like dust on a jewel," Chang-Diaz said. "You think how easy it would be to wipe off that dust. . . . Our planet is so fragile. We need to care for it! We're not just citizens of a country. We're also citizens of planet Earth."

Chang-Diaz was born in Costa Rica, Central America. He grew up in Connecticut. He earned the highest degree in physics at a top American school. Physics deals with how things move: how fast, how far, how straight. Those are huge concerns in rocket science. A rocket explodes with the power of many nuclear bombs. And sometimes there are astronauts sitting on top of it.

Chang-Diaz became one of those astronauts in 1981. In 1989 he and his crew launched the probe *Galileo*, which went to Jupiter. In 1994 he took part in a historic mission. Russia and the United States, former enemies, conducted the mission together.

Between flights, Chang-Diaz is designing a better way to blast humans into space on top of exploding rockets. His system is more reliable and easier to control. It will help future explorers travel to Mars.

"Space is so new," Chang-Diaz said. "I'm a dreamer. I long for the day when we can go on long-distance voyages to other planets and stars."

Dear NASA

In the twenty-first century, NASA plans to send astronauts to Mars. The mission could take several years. But the explorers will be the first humans to leave our Earth-moon system. Would you want to be one of them? Write a letter to accept or turn down the job.

Dear NASA:

When it comes to space, I'm most interested in _____

_____

_____

_____

I would/would not (circle one) like to go to Mars because _____

_____

_____

_____

The worst part of the Mars mission would be _____

_____

_____

_____

The best part would be _____

_____

_____

_____

Sincerely,

_____

(Your Name)

Explorers of the Future
This Means You!

Soon you and your friends will be the explorers of planet Earth. Where will you go? What will you see? Our planet has plenty of deserts to cross and mountains to climb. But many future missions will go deep into the ocean and farther into space. NASA has plans for a trip to take humans to Mars.

Suppose you could travel in time. Would you want to explore in the past, present, or future? Read about the good and bad parts, below. Write what you think will happen in the future. Then fill in the Explorer Job Application.

Past

Good Side:

Very little land on Earth has been explored. You can be the first person to reach a goal such as the North Pole. You will gain fame and a place in history. You'll see land that no one has seen before. You can name all the mountains, lakes, and so on.

Bad Side:

Exploring unknown land is very risky. You don't know what pitfalls lie ahead. There are no tracks or roads to follow. You have no radio to call for help. There are no airplanes to pick you up. Your clothes and equipment are basic. The risk of dying is great.

Present

Good Side:

If something goes wrong, you can radio for help. Planes and helicopters can pick you up. Satellites can track your position. Your equipment is more advanced. Knowledge of the area can help you avoid mistakes.

Bad Side:

Other explorers have been to famous places, such as the North Pole and even outer space. So you probably won't make history.

Future

Good Side: _____

_____

_____

_____

Bad Side: _____

_____

_____

_____

EXPLORER JOB APPLICATION

I am applying for a job as an explorer in the [past, present, future].

The reason I prefer this time period is _____

_____

_____

The part of the Earth I would most like to explore is _____

_____

The reason is _____

_____

_____

The part I would least like to explore is _____

_____

The reason is _____

_____

_____

My skills or experience that will help me in this job include _____

_____

_____

_____

_____

Leif Erikson
c.1000

Juan Ponce de León
1513

Hernando Cortez
1519

Sir Francis Drake
1577

Giovanni Verrazano
1524

Samuel de Champlain
1599

1000   1400   1500   1600

Christopher Columbus
1492

John Cabot
1497

Jacques Cartier
1535

Henry Hudson
1610

Hernando de Soto
1539

Robert de La Salle
1681

Estevanico
1539

Francisco Coronado
1540

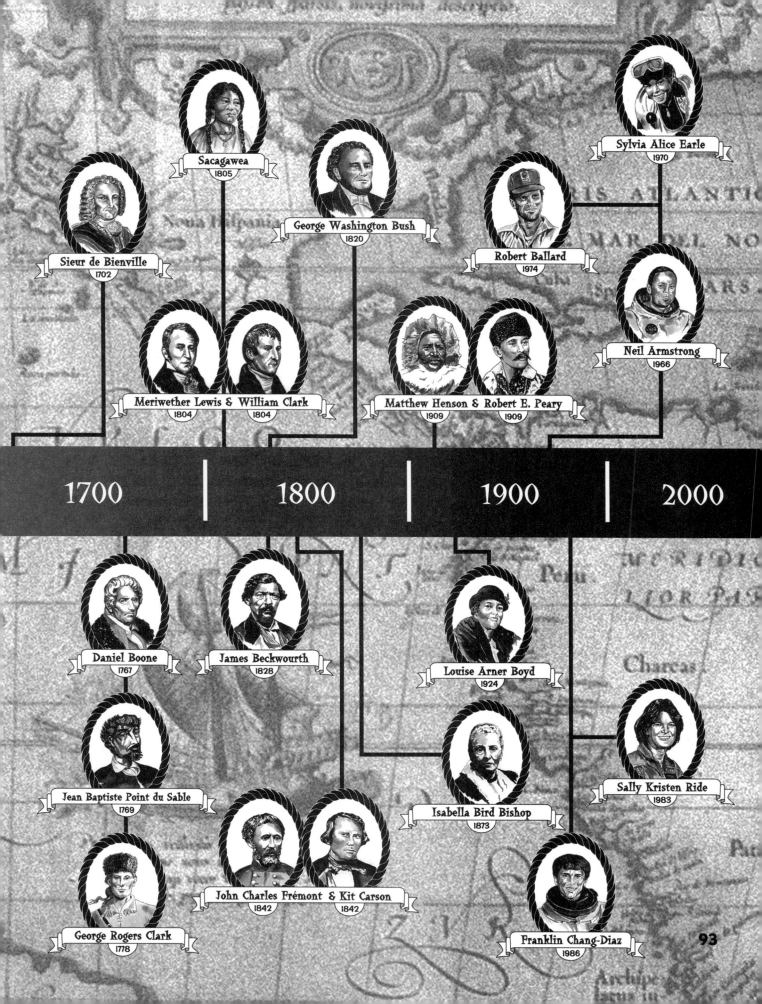

Sylvia Alice Earle
1970

Sacagawea
1805

Sieur de Bienville
1702

George Washington Bush
1820

Robert Ballard
1974

Neil Armstrong
1966

Meriwether Lewis & William Clark
1804   1804

Matthew Henson & Robert E. Peary
1909   1909

1700   1800   1900   2000

Daniel Boone
1767

James Beckwourth
1828

Louise Arner Boyd
1924

Jean Baptiste Point du Sable
1769

Isabella Bird Bishop
1873

Sally Kristen Ride
1983

George Rogers Clark
1778

John Charles Frémont & Kit Carson
1842   1842

Franklin Chang-Diaz
1986

93

World Map

Beaufort
Sea

Baffin Bay

Greenland
Sea

Bering Sea

Hudson
Bay

Labrador
Sea

Gulf of
Alaska

**NORTH
AMERICA**

Gulf of
Mexico

ATLANTIC
OCEAN

Caribbean Sea

**SOUTH
AMERICA**

PACIFIC
OCEAN

ARCTIC OCEAN

Norwegian
Sea

North
Sea

EUROPE

ASIA

Mediterranean
Sea

AFRICA

Arabian
Sea

PACIFIC
OCEAN

AUSTRALIA

INDIAN
OCEAN

Tasman
Sea

ANTARCTICA

ANSWERS

My First Colony, *Page 12*
Items colonists can make on site or that aren't
necessities include
Firewood
Lumber for Houses
Jewelry
Trinkets
Furniture
Pots and Pans
The trinkets, jewelry, and pots and pans could be
traded for food and other necessary items. Student
answers may vary.

Place Names, *Page 19*
1E. Florida—Land of Flowers
2J. Colorado—Red
3I. Montana—Mountain
4D. Mesa—Plateau
5G. Los Angeles—The Angels
6A. Buena Vista—Beautiful View
7B. Salinas—Salt Mines
8C. El Paso—The Pass
9H. Amarillo—Yellow
10F. Cuba—Cask

Most Spanish names appear in the states of Florida,
Texas, Arizona, New Mexico, and California because
that's where Spanish explorers claimed land.

Upstream, Downstream, *Page 27*
1b. All rivers flow out to an ocean or to a land-
locked valley.
2a. The river gets its water from the Great Lakes.
Also, rivers are fresh because they are constantly
moving. Instead of settling on the bottom, miner-
als such as salt get carried along by the current.
3a. Rivers also receive a small amount of water
directly from precipitation.
4c. More water has to flow down about the same
amount of space.

Afloat in a Boat, *Page 33*
Answers will vary. If explorers think they will be rescued, they'll probably opt for food and first aid. If they
think their only escape is to navigate out, they'll opt
for navigation tools. With no hope of rescue, food will
only prolong the misery. Remind students that lemon
juice prevents scurvy, butter is very high in fat and
calories, the boat is surrounded by fresh water (Hudson
Bay), blankets will keep them warm and so reduce the
number of calories they use up.

The Mighty Mississippi, *Page 35*
Baton Rouge, Natchez, Vicksburg, Greenville, Helena,
Memphis, Cairo, Cape Girardeau, St. Louis, Hannibal,
Quincy, Keokuk, Davenport, Rock Island, Dubuque, La
Crosse, Minneapolis/St. Paul, St. Cloud. The source is
west of Hibbing, Minnesota. Ten states and two capi-
tals (Baton Rouge and St. Paul) touch the Mississippi.

Parlez-Vous Français?, *Page 37*
1E. Montréal—Royal Mountain
2I. Detroit—Strait
3J. Louisville—Town of King Louis
4H. Trois Rivières—Three Rivers
5F. Montpelier—Pelier Mountain
6D. Baton Rouge—Red Stick (or baton)
7B. Terre Haute—High Land
8C. La Crosse—The Cross
9G. Eau Claire—Clear Water
10A. Des Moines—Of the Monks

A Beast to Remember, *Page 43*
The beast is a bison, the first the explorers had ever
seen.

Where in the World Is Isabella Bird?, *Page 69*
1D. Auckland is the capital of New Zealand.
2C. Morocco is the only North African country
listed.
3A. The Yangtze and Shanghai are major sites in
China.
4F. The Big Island of Hawaii has active volcanoes
such as Moana Loa.
5G. Yaks live only in extremely high altitude regions.
6H. The Rocky Mountains are in the United States.
7B. Malaysia fits the description.
8E. Iraq, Iran, and Kurdistan were all once called
Persia.

Risky or Reckless?, *Page 81*
Answers will vary. For example, if students are expert
skateboarders, the first item is risky; if not, it's reckless. Some things, such as eating spoiled meat and
going out in winter without mittens, are reckless for
all; there's no reward to balance the risk.

Lucky 13, *Page 87*
Students' answers may vary—a good spark for
debate. Space: all; Ocean: all but air and (possibly)
food; Islands: transportation; Desert: transportation
and possibly shelter, food, and water; Arctic: all but air
and water (can melt snow); Woods: transportation.